NORTH STAFFORDSHIRE CO
ON THE HILL NORTH OF CHELL

Being a history of the mines and railways at
Chell, Turnhurst, Oxford, Wedgwood and Newchapel,
situated at the northernmost extremity of the
North Staffordshire Coalfield

Allan C. Baker

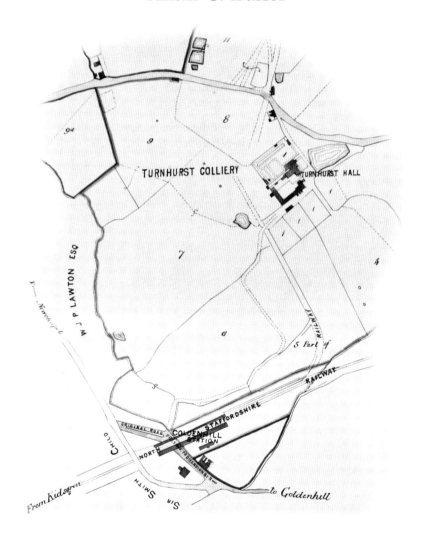

© Lightmoor Press & Allan C. Baker 2014. Designed by Neil Parkhouse

British Library Cataloguing-in-Publication Data. A catalogue record for this book is available from the British Library

ISBN 13: 9781899889 84 6

LIGHTMOOR PRESS
Unit 144B, Lydney Trading Estate, Harbour Road, Lydney, Gloucestershire GL15 5EJ
www.lightmoor.co.uk

LIGHTMOOR PRESS is an imprint of BLACK DWARF LIGHTMOOR PUBLICATIONS LTD
Printed by BERFORTS INFORMATION PRESS, Oxford

CONTENTS

PREFACE .... PAGE 2

I: SETTING THE SCENE .... PAGE 3

II: THE MAIN-LINE RAILWAYS & CANALS: PROJECTED & BUILT .... PAGE 5

III: COAL & IRONSTONE MINING .... PAGE 9

IV: WEDGWOOD, LANE ENDS & BRINDLEY FORD COLLIERIES .... PAGE 15

V: THE TURNHURST HALL COAL & IRONSTONE COMPANY .... PAGE 21

VI: THE TUNSTALL COAL & IRON COMPANY LTD & ITS PREDECESSORS.... PAGE 27

VII: ROBERT HEATH & SONS LTD:
        OPERATIONS AT NEWCHAPEL, LANE ENDS & TURNHURST .... PAGE 47

VIII: THE FINAL YEARS & A FEW ODD ITEMS .... PAGE 57

ACKNOWLEDGEMENTS.. PAGE 59

APPENDIX I: MAP REFERENCES FOR THE PRINCIPAL MINING SITES MENTIONED IN THE TEXT .... PAGE 60

APPENDIX II: LIST OF PLANT & MACHINERY, ETC AT CHELL AND TURNHURST COLLIERIES 1899.. PAGE 61

APPENDIX III: THE SCENE TODAY .... PAGE 62

ENDNOTES: .... PAGE 63

In the text, amounts of money are quoted in the pre-decimal currency of pounds, shillings and pence (£ s d). Rather than reinterpret this every time as pounds and new pence (£ p), which has little relevance anyway without taking into account the effects of decades of inflation, a brief conversion scale is given here:
In pre-decimal mony: £1 = 20 shillings; 1 shilling = 12 pence (d)
Decimal conversions: 1 shilling = 5 new pence (p);
10 shillings = 50p; 6d = 2.5p
£1 in 1900 is worth approximately £60 today

DEDICATION

To my late Father, Stephen Allan Baker, who taught me so much, took me to so many places and introduced me to so many people, encouraging, helping and supporting me endlessly.
I know he would have loved and treasured this book.

PREFACE

I have enjoyed putting these notes together, as the area around Chell and Newchapel, north of Stoke-on-Trent, is one that has always fascinated me. I recall many a happy summer evening exploring, on some occasions with my late father, when much remained to be seen of the former mining activities and railways. My father had told me about the delightful locomotives, with lovely mellow whistles, built by Robert Heath & Sons of the Black Bull and Ford Green ironworks in the Biddulph Valley. These locomotives had been built in the workshops at Black Bull and several of them survived until the early 1960s. With particular affection, I remember a very pleasant couple of hours Dad and I spent one evening watching them at work. Thanks to a kindly crew, we had a ride on one of the six-wheelers, No. 15 dating from 1915, and later we delved into the locomotive shed where several other locomotives were lurking, at least one of which had been in use earlier that day. Anyone who has ever entered an industrial locomotive shed where engines had been put away for the night will be familiar with the unforgettable and welcoming atmosphere. The lovely smells, the steam leaking here and there, and the gurgles as the engines cooled down, added to perhaps by the excitement of discovering something new lurking away in the distant depths. At the time I was learning how to drive so these excursions doubled-up as driving lessons under my father's pupilage.

I owe a great debt of gratitude to my late father. Although not a native, his knowledge of North Staffordshire was phenomenal and he never stinted in encouraging and supporting my interest in the area I love so much. Over the succeeding forty-odd years, I have collected anything and everything in connection with this area that came my way, until recently making a determined effort to place it all on record. Marshalling the information and facts into a coherent narrative has not been an easy task. However, I hope my readers will feel the end result acceptable, as only they can be my judge. I have not provided a Bibliography, as all the volumes I have consulted in any depth are quoted in the footnotes. I should add, at this juncture, that I make no claim for completeness in my researches and while the history of mining operations in the area goes back well into the 14th century – and maybe earlier – my story largely concentrates on activities in the 'Railway Age'. Of course, any opinions expressed are mine and mine alone, as is the responsibility for any errors of fact or presentation. I do, however, hope that my readers find some enjoyment in following the somewhat convoluted story of the mines and railways 'On the hill north of Chell'. It goes without saying that if anybody has anything to add or to amend my story, I shall be only too pleased to hear from them via the publisher.

Allan C Baker,
High Halden, Kent, November 2013

I

SETTING THE SCENE

Climbing from the Staffordshire pottery town of Stoke-upon-Trent, which stands at around 400 feet above sea level, a ridge of high ground extends through the other pottery towns north of Stoke to Chell.[1] Onwards, it continues via Packmoor, Newchapel and Mow Cop, with its famous folly[2] that can be seen for miles around, towards the Cheshire plain. Bearing slightly to the east, it continues along Congleton Edge forming the county boundary, to terminate rather abruptly at Cloud End, yet another famous landmark that dominates the scenery thereabouts. Here it forms the division between the watersheds of the rivers Trent and Mersey. Between Chell and Newchapel,[3] its average maximum height is approximately 700 feet above sea level, although Mow Cop itself stands at almost 1,100 feet. It is flanked to the east by the Biddulph Valley, along which flows the infant Trent rising on Biddulph Moor[4], while to the west there is a dip in the high ground before Harecastle Hill and, thereafter, a steep descent into the Chatterley Valley. Both sides of the ridge are at around 550 feet above sea level and on both sides the North Staffordshire Railway (NSR) constructed lines. In the case of the Biddulph Valley, this was largely to tap the mineral wealth about which this book is mainly concerned, while on the other side of the hill, the Potteries Loop Line, as it came to be known, also served the industrial and personal transport needs of the local population.

On this ridge of high ground between Chell and Newchapel, a number of mining operations developed most of which, after the coming of the railways, had need to transport their output down the slopes by building several connecting railways of one sort or another. With tongue in cheek it might have been better if the owners had adopted a practice used in for example, the north-eastern Assam Coalfield, where the shafts are sometimes driven into the bottom of the hills and then go upwards, rather than the reverse. It would certainly have saved transport costs, although as it happened, the seams of coal in question did not easily lend themselves to this type of extraction. However, this method was used to extract coal from seams discovered when the first Harecastle Tunnel was being driven on the Grand Trunk Canal,[5] which was completed in 1777.

As a matter of interest, many of the important seams of coal and ironstone in the North Staffordshire Coalfield – and there are many – can be found in Harecastle Hill. The nearest of the pottery towns is Tunstall, northernmost of the six and, in the words of the novelist Arnold Bennett in his stories of the Five Towns, the extremity of civilisation in those parts. The County Borough of Stoke-on-Trent was formed by Federation in 1911; it was later raised to the status of a city by the late King George V when he visited the area in 1925. It consists of the six towns of Burslem, Stoke-upon-Trent, Hanley, Longton, Tunstall and Fenton. Bennett, however, omitted Fenton in his novels; needless to say, the local inhabitants have never forgiven him. In 1841, the townships of Great and Little Chell in the Parish of Wolstanton covered a surface area of 740 acres and, by 1901, had a population of 3,502.[6]

The seams of coal and ironstone involved were, in order starting from the surface, the Winghay, Rowhurst, Burnwood and Twist. The Rusty Mine or Winghay ironstone, along with the Brown Mine ironstone, lies between the top two, while the Burnwood ironstone is above the Burnwood coal. All the seams, coal and ironstone, outcropped around the site of Wedgwood Colliery. The method of working was to allow the coal and ironstone as it was got to gravitate down to the pit shafts. This allowed greater reserves of coal to be available without having to draw the coal up inclined underground 'dips' within the seams themselves. This is best illustrated on the diagram below.[7]

The mining operations we are here concerned with were for both coal and perhaps to an equal extent, ironstone, the latter abounding in this section of the mineral field. The seams of coal and ironstone are located east of a north-south fault, known as the High Lane Fault,[8] in the North Staffordshire, or to give it its more popular name, Pottery Coalfield. They are in the middle coal measures on the eastern side of the syncline,[9] dipping down at about 1 in 4 to the west-south-west.[10] The coal would have been sold locally at Chell and surrounding villages, short horse and cart journeys for most of the pits, while the bulk of the ironstone would probably have been taken by similar means to the Clough Hall Ironworks of the Kinnersly[11] family. This was a mile or so to the north at Kidsgrove. Mining in these parts for coal and ironstone

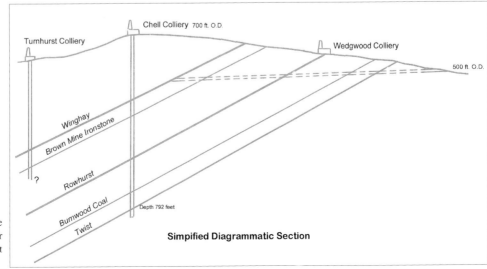

A simplified diagrammatic section of the principal coal and ironstone seams and their inclination, for Wedgwood, Chell and Turnhurst collieries.

HARRISEAHEAD. COLLIERY.

goes back to at least the 1340s, although our story starts much later in the 1850s. At this time, North Staffordshire generated a surfeit of ironstone, such that significant quantities were transported to ironworks to the south of the county. However, coal was at a premium, despite extensive reserves. There were around 800 pottery kilns in and around the six towns and the numerous villages that later formed the County Borough of Stoke-on-Trent. All these kilns were coal-fired and with the multifarious other uses for the fuel, there were frequent shortages, especially for domestic use in the winter months. The existing ironworks in North Staffordshire, of which Clough Hall was but one of several, largely consumed all the coal their proprietors were able to mine from pits they owned or leased. There was thus a growing incentive to develop main line railways, to tap those areas not already served where the coal seams were located.

Unfortunately we do not have photographs of any of the collieries with which this book is primarily concerned. However, this photograph of Harriseahead Colliery near Newchapel in 1910, within sight of the Turnhurst and Chell pits, and in operation at the same period, probably gives a reasonable indication of what some of the surface equipment at the pits we are concerned with would have looked like. Notice the pit cage and the large stack of coal in the foreground. In 1921, 105 men and boys were employed underground at this pit, in addition to 22 surface workers above.
JOHN RYAN COLLECTION

II
THE MAIN LINE RAILWAYS AND CANALS: PROJECTED AND BUILT

Although mining operations in this area predate the railway era, this book largely confines itself to the period covered by the developing main line railways. A brief outline of the two NSR lines referred to in Chapter I is therefore necessary to help readers understanding. There were a number of schemes put forward during the canal and early railway eras to improve transport in the Biddulph Valley. The town of Biddulph is about eight miles north from Stoke town centre as the crow flies and some three quarters of the way to Congleton, where the valley effectively ends. As early as 1801, there was a scheme for a railway from the Caldon Canal at Foxley,[12] northwards along the valley some three miles and five furlongs to Brindley Ford. At that point, two branches were proposed to serve local coal mines.[13] The first half mile or so of this projected line was later followed by the Foxley Branch of the Caldon Canal. We do not know precisely when this private branch canal was built but it would have been around 1804. It served a number of relatively small individual mining operations in and around Ford Green and, in 1863, was extended a short distance to serve the Ford Green Ironworks and collieries of Robert Heath – of which more anon. By this time, the Caldon Canal, as part of the Trent & Mersey system, was owned by the NSR, so the cost was shared between Heath and the railway company.

In 1838, another railway was proposed, attacking the valley from the opposite end as a feeder of traffic to the Macclesfield Canal rather than the Caldon.[14] Promoted as the Buglawton & Biddulph Valley Railway, the main line was intended to run from the canal at Buglawton, just north of Congleton, three miles and 70 chains to Knypersley. Four branches were proposed, serving a stone quarry to the east at Trough,[15] along with collieries at Woodhouse, Gillow Heath and Falls; there were a number of other small coal winnings hereabouts that might also have benefitted from the railway. As was the case with the main line, the gradients on the branches were severe, in the case of the one to the stone quarries between 1 in 12 and 1 in 22, and it was over a mile long. A number of the coal workings already had primitive tramways to connect with nearby roads and the proposed line would have made contact with some of them. Among the larger of the collieries was the one at Falls, just south of Gillow Heath, developed and owned by Hugh Henshall Williamson, whom we shall meet again later in these pages. The Batemans, another family we have yet to meet, owned some of the others, along with John Bailey, and Charles and James Lancaster.[16] The engineer was Charles Nichols and the surveyor Samuel Taylor. Like the earlier scheme, despite the plans and

sections, books of reference, etc. being deposited with Parliament, nothing came of it. The plans, incidentally, describe the proposal as *'a Railway from Dane Henshaw to Biddulph'*.[17] Unlike the earlier scheme, which appears to have been largely promoted by the Trent & Mersey Canal Company (as owners of the Caldon Canal), this scheme was the initiative of a group of local businessmen, including those mentioned above, with interests in the various coal mines and the stone quarry it was intended to serve.[18]

The development of the main line railways to serve the area was the cause of much agitation with the population of Congleton, the Biddulph Valley and surrounding area. With the NSR apparently reluctant to do anything, a group of local businessmen decided to act. Included in their number was John Batemen (1782-1858)

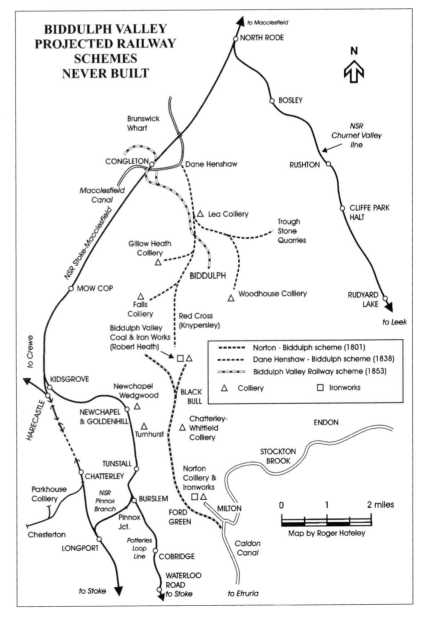

and his son James (2nd, 1811-1897) of Knypersley Hall and later Biddulph Grange, large land owners in the Biddulph area. John's father James (1st, 1749-1824), an engineer and iron founder of Salford, bought the estate from the Gresley family in 1808, making further local land acquisitions in 1810 and 1812.[19] Unlike his son, however, he never moved from Salford. With the backing of the Mayor of Congleton and other local businessmen, in 1853 the group promoted the Biddulph Valley Railway Company, which was provisionally registered on 5th July that year, under the Joint Stock Companies Registration Act of 1845. The original intention was to build a line from the NSR main line at Congleton, along the valley via Biddulph, Ford Green and Fenton, to rejoin the NSR at or near Stoke-upon-Trent. It was later decided that, rather than form a limited company, a statutory body by Act of Parliament would be a better mechanism, as was the case with most railway schemes intended for public use. By the time the plans and sections, books of reference, etc. were deposited with Parliament on 30th November 1853, the scheme had been truncated. With the title of the Congleton & Biddulph Valley Railway (C&BVR), the plan was to build a line from Congleton via Gillow Heath to Red Cross, near Knypersley.[20] The main line would have been almost four miles long, running from a junction with the NSR Stoke to Macclesfield line just south of Congleton station. Three branches were included, one of which would have served the centre of Congleton, as the existing NSR line skirted the town to its east. A second served a wharf on the Macclesfield Canal, while a third connected with some coal mining operations just north of Biddulph, at Lea Forge. The principal purpose of the line, however, was to serve several coal mines around Knypersley, as indeed had been the intention of the earlier proposed railways which would have connected with the canals.[21] The capital was £35,000 and the consulting engineer was the well established railway civil engineer John E. Errington,[22] although he appointed an 'acting' engineer to undertake the legwork, one John Myatt. The promoters did well to enlist the services of Errington, who had worked for much of his career with the celebrated railway builder Joseph Locke.[23]

This local activity prompted the NSR into action, not wanting

rival railways in what was considered its own territory. It has to be added that this was neither the first nor, as events turned out, the last occasion on which the NSR was spurred into action by rival schemes to protect its closely guarded boundaries. With the support of the NSR, the Potteries, Biddulph & Congleton Mineral Railway Company was provisionally registered on 30th October 1853, also under the Joint Stock Companies Registration Act, to build a line from Stoke-upon-Trent along the Biddulph Valley to Congleton. Notice that once again it was intended to form a limited company to develop the proposals, rather than a statutory body by Act of Parliament. This was despite primary legislation being necessary for the compulsory land purchase powers required to enable the line to be built. Notice too that, by its very title, there was no intention at this stage to provide a passenger service. It is interesting to speculate why a separate company was planned to build and operate the proposed railway. There is no doubt, however, that the NSR was behind the registration of the company, as the subscribers were the railway company's solicitors, William Keary and John Sheppard. The plans, sections and other documents were deposited with Parliament on 13th November 1853 and both schemes went forward as the promoters of the C&BVR appear to have been unconvinced that the NSR would in fact build its proposed line. A House of Lords select committee was nominated to review both Bills and this sat on 19th and 20th June 1854, with Lord Stanley in the chair. In the event, however, the C&BVR promoters offered no evidence and the only objection to the NSR scheme was by the Manchester, Sheffield & Lincolnshire Railway (MS&LR), concerned about the proposed branch to the Macclesfield Canal, which it owned.[24] John Curphey Forsyth, the NSR engineer, and William Keary, its solicitor, gave evidence and with the MS&LR satisfied by a number of clauses to protect its interests, the Bill was reported to the House. Clearly there had been some behind the scenes activity, as the C&BVR Bill, which had its first reading by the Lords on 9th February, was ordered to be withdrawn by the same body on 28th June, the NSR Bill going forward to receive the Royal Assent on 24th July 1854.[25] This followed an agreement in committee for the C&BVR Bill to be withdrawn on the understanding the NSR one went forward. The NSR scheme

A poor quality but rare photograph of the remains of the Foxley Branch of the Caldon Canal at Norton, in about 1952. Beyond this point, which is where the canal passed under the Hanley to Leek road, the present A53, the waterway was completely weed infested. It was the approximate site of this canal that the 1801 proposal for a railway to Biddulph would have followed at the start of its route. The dirt tip is for Norton Colliery, while on the left are the slag remains from the former ironworks, which closed in 1928. The brook to the left, passing under the road bridge, flowed into the River Trent, itself not far behind where the photographer was standing.
Dr Jack Hollick

included several branches, two at its southern end that need not detain us here, one to a goods and mineral wharf at Buglawton (Brunswick Wharf), a little to the north of Congleton and another to the Macclesfield Canal, as briefly mentioned above.[26]

Being pre-occupied with long and sometimes acrimonious negotiations regarding a possible amalgamation with the London & North Western Railway (L&NWR), the NSR directors made no attempt to hurry themselves in building the line. As the estimated cost of £190,000 was more than covered by the capital the Company was empowered to raise under its existing legislation, the directors declined to obtain powers to increase the capital under the new Act. Notwithstanding this, they did seem reluctant to raise the cash, claiming after they did, that in waiting for more favourable times the money had been raised on better terms. However, both Forsyth and Keary made great play before the Select Committee of how important it was to develop the coal reserves of the Biddulph Valley, due to the general shortage of coal in the area as alluded to above. A railway they said, was the only way to encourage the coal owners to develop the industry in the area. It was not until March 1858 that tenders for its construction were considered, a delay resulting in the line being opened no fewer than three times! The first sod was cut by John Bateman on 27th April 1858, shortly before he died, near the site of Robert Heath's new ironworks, at what was referred to as Childerplay but was perhaps more appropriately Black Bull.[27] To meet the Parliamentary time limit for its construction, it was officially opened on 3rd August 1859. This was important, as the Act imposed a penalty on the railway company for non-compliance and, moreover, it placed a restriction on paying dividends on its share capital if the line was not completed.[28] Traffic did start to flow, 8,244 tons of mineral traffic being reported in the period 1st August to 22nd October 1859 for example,[29] despite the contractor still being on site. However, it was not until 28th August 1860 before the contractors, William & Solomon Tredwell, reported the works complete. The third event took place on 1st June 1864, when the line was opened for passenger traffic. Although the details need not concern us here, getting Board of Trade approval for passenger traffic was a lengthy process taking almost a year. Several visits by the Inspecting Officer, Captain Henry Tyler, were necessary as the NSR, somewhat reluctantly, complied with his various requirements.[30]

The line was 12 miles and 63 chains long, running from Stoke to a junction with the NSR line to Macclesfield at Congleton Upper Junction. There was a branch from what became known as the Lower Junction, one mile and four chains long, to a goods and mineral wharf at Brunswick; this was a little north of the town. A second branch, albeit just a short spur, ran from the Lower Junction to a wharf on the Macclesfield Canal. Single track throughout, although the earthworks and bridges were for the most part constructed to allow for a double line of rails, it was converted to double track in stages as traffic increased. The section from Stoke to what became

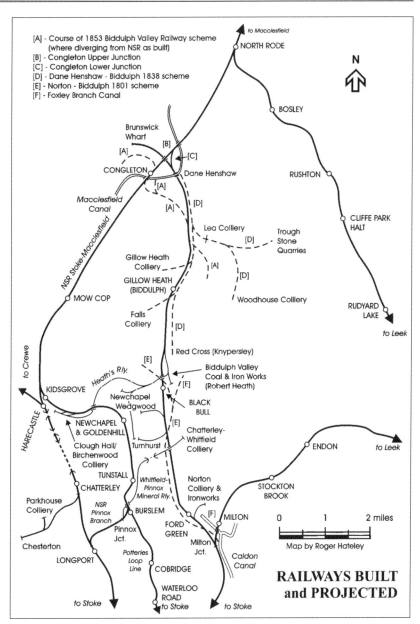

[A] - Course of 1853 Biddulph Valley Railway scheme (where diverging from NSR as built)
[B] - Congleton Upper Junction
[C] - Congleton Lower Junction
[D] - Dane Henshaw - Biddulph 1838 scheme
[E] - Norton - Biddulph 1801 scheme
[F] - Foxley Branch Canal

Map by Roger Hateley

RAILWAYS BUILT and PROJECTED

Milton Junction was converted in 1867, coinciding with the opening of the branch from Milton to Leek on 12th November that year; conversion from Milton Junction to Chell was completed on 1st October 1883 and finally to Heath Junction,[31] at Black Bull, on 1st December 1883. The section thence to Congleton remained single track. In view of the local topography, the gradients on the line were severe. Climbing almost the entire distance to its summit at Heath Junction (Black Bull), the four miles from Milton Junction were largely at 1 in 89 but there were sections further south at Bucknall as steep as 1 in 50. Descending to Congleton, there were long sections at 1 in 78 and 1 in 56, with the descent to Brunswick Wharf and the climb from the Lower to Upper Junctions at Congleton at 1 in 45. Fortunately, for the vast bulk of loaded mineral traffic the grades were favourable but the line was no sinecure to operate, especially with the loose coupled mineral trains, a type of train that dominated the traffic.

The other NSR line that need only concern us briefly was the Potteries Loop Line, running to the west of the high ground at Chell. This line started life as a branch from the main line between Stoke and Kidsgrove at Etruria, to serve Earl Granville's Ironworks and collieries at Etruria and Shelton. Opened in June 1850, it was extended to Hanley in December 1861[32] and onwards in parts, culminating with the section from Goldenhill to Kidsgrove, where it rejoined the main line to Macclesfield, on 15th November 1875. The line was always intended for both goods and passenger traffic, and was double track throughout. Having said that, there was in fact little other than passenger traffic north of Pitts Hill and the section from Goldenhill to Kidsgrove was converted to single track in 1909. Because the Loop Line passed through the Clough Hall Estate, part of the agreement with the Kinnerslys was the provision of a separate line to serve the works. There was, therefore, a third set of rails from Kidsgrove to just short of Goldenhill, where a connection with the works lines was made. Known somewhat obviously as 'The Third Line', it remained in situ to serve the later Birchenwood Colliery and coking plant which was located on the same estate. It continued to be worked from Kidsgrove as a completely independent single line until the Loop Line closed to through traffic in 1966.[33]

One person consistently chivvying the NSR directors to get on with building the Biddulph Branch was Robert Heath (2nd, 1816-1893), mentioned briefly above, as in September 1857, he leased a large tract of minerals under the Knypersley Hall Estate from the Bateman family.[34] As early as 1858, Heath was planning an ironworks and sinking pits in and around Black Bull for coal and ironstone, as well as developing existing ones. In December, he applied to the NSR for siding accommodation, which was agreed in June the following year; however, the agreement was not signed until April 1861. Heath was not long in expanding his interests in the Biddulph Valley, acquiring mineral rights to the south in the Norton and Ford Green area. Ralph Sneyd, along with the Chetwynd, Sparrow and Adderley families, were the principal landowners thereabouts. In December 1861, Heath asked the NSR for siding accommodation at Ford Green, which was also agreed[35]. As well as extensive coal and ironstone mining, Heath built ironworks, forges and rolling mills at both Black Bull and Ford Green. Between the two works in the days before the First World War, Robert Heath & Sons was reputed to have been amongst the largest manufacturers of bar iron in the country and, it has even been said, the world. Personally, I feel this rather ambitious statement would be difficult to prove one way or the other. For many years, Robert Heath & Sons Ltd, as the firm later became, generated the largest amount of goods and mineral traffic on the Biddulph Valley line. As well as traffic conveyed by the NSR, the company operated inter-works traffic with its own locomotives, including supplying coal wharfs at Brindley Ford, Bradley Green and the Brunswick Wharf in Congleton.[36] In the main, the operations at both sites were on the east side of the line but bridges were later constructed to take internal works lines over the NSR as operations extended to the west side. In the three months ending 30th September 1861, compared with the same period the previous year, the traffic on the branch increased from 19,000 to 24,500 tons, with an increase in NSR revenue from £2,220 to £2,700.[37]

BIDDULPH VALLEY IRONWORKS.

B.228.

The Biddulph Valley Ironworks and collieries of Robert Heath & Sons Ltd in their heyday. The view is looking due north and was taken in about 1905. In the background, to the right of the left hand set of headsticks – local parlance for the pithead hauling equipment – can be seen the folly at Mow Cop, which was, and indeed still is, famous for miles around. The left hand set of headsticks served the Victoria Pit, a downcast dating from 1847, when it was sunk to a depth of 80 yards and named Magpie Pit. It was deepened to 130 yards in 1860 and again to 475 yards in 1898, and its name was then changed to commemorate Queen Victoria's Golden Jubilee the previous year. The other shaft is the Havelock, an upcast sunk in 1861 to 255 yards when it was known as the Deep Bye Pit; it too was deepened to 475 yards in 1898. The four blast furnaces and associated stoves are to the left, with the NSR Biddulph Valley line in a deep cutting as it climbed out of the valley, to the left of and behind the furnaces. WARRILLOW COLLECTION, KEELE UNIVERSITY LIBRARY

III
COAL AND IRONSTONE MINING

One particular mining operation needs to concern us before we move on to the main purpose of this book. At Chell, or more accurately Fegg Hayes, was the Whitfield Colliery of Hugh Henshall Williamson and his brother Edward; it was situated immediately on the east side of the Biddulph Valley line. In June 1861, the brothers requested siding accommodation with the new railway and this was agreed in November.[38] In April 1872, the Chatterley Iron Company acquired Whitfield Colliery and after a number of vicissitudes, including a bankruptcy, Chatterley-Whitfield Collieries Ltd was formed in January 1891. However, prior to this in 1878, in order to avoid some of the NSR charges for the movement of its traffic, the vast majority of which was coal for shipment via the Mersey ports, a private mineral line had been built. Two miles and 55 chains long, it ran from the colliery due west to Tunstall and by this route, a distance of 11 miles for traffic heading north via the NSR at Stoke was avoided. Connection was made at Tunstall with the NSR Pinnox Branch,

itself connected at Longport with the main line north to Crewe and Macclesfield. The colliery line had to cross the high ground referred to earlier and in doing so had steep gradients for both loaded and empty wagons, as well as a 404 yard tunnel under High Lane.[39] After completion of the colliery line, traffic from Whitfield Colliery via the Biddulph Valley line was comparatively small.[40]

Several mining operations are of concern to us. The principal pits were named variously as Chell, Oxford, Turnhurst, Rising Lark, Wedgwood, Lane Ends and Newchapel, along with associated coal wharfs, and both standard and narrow gauge railways. However, both Robert Heath & Sons and Chatterley-Whitfield Collieries have a place in the story too. Some of the operations made railway connection with the Biddulph Valley route and others with the Potteries Loop Line. As already mentioned, mining operations in the area go back a long way. However, in so far as any of what might be termed extensive workings are concerned, they probably originated with the famous canal engineer James Brindley (1716-1772) and his associates. Brindley had married

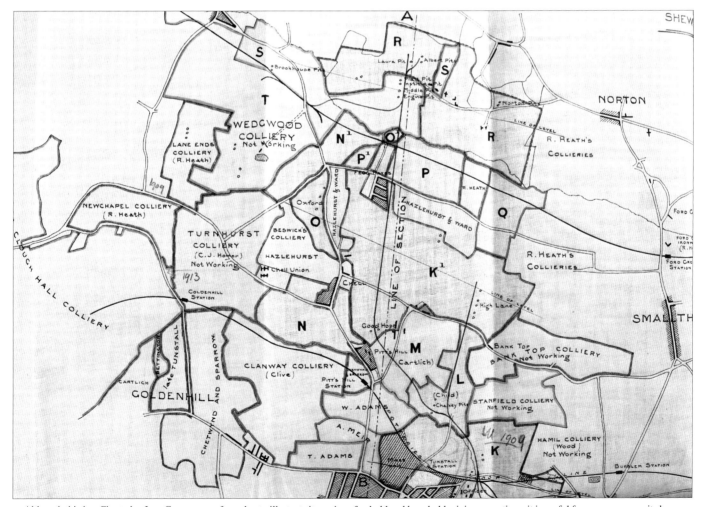

Although this is a Chatterley Iron Company surface plan to illustrate its various freehold and leasehold mining operations, it is useful for our purpose as it shows the location of most of the collieries that are the subject of this book, or are otherwise mentioned in the text. It is signed by Edward Brownfield Wain, the general manager of the Iron Company. COURTESY STAFFORDSHIRE COUNTY RECORD OFFICE: SCRO: D1133/CW1

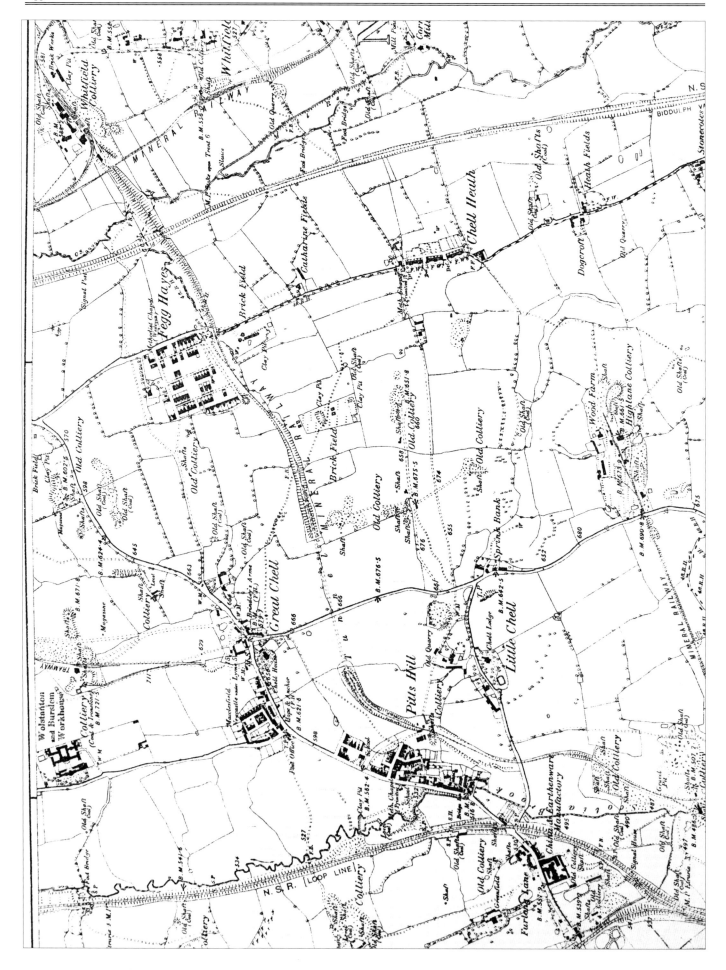

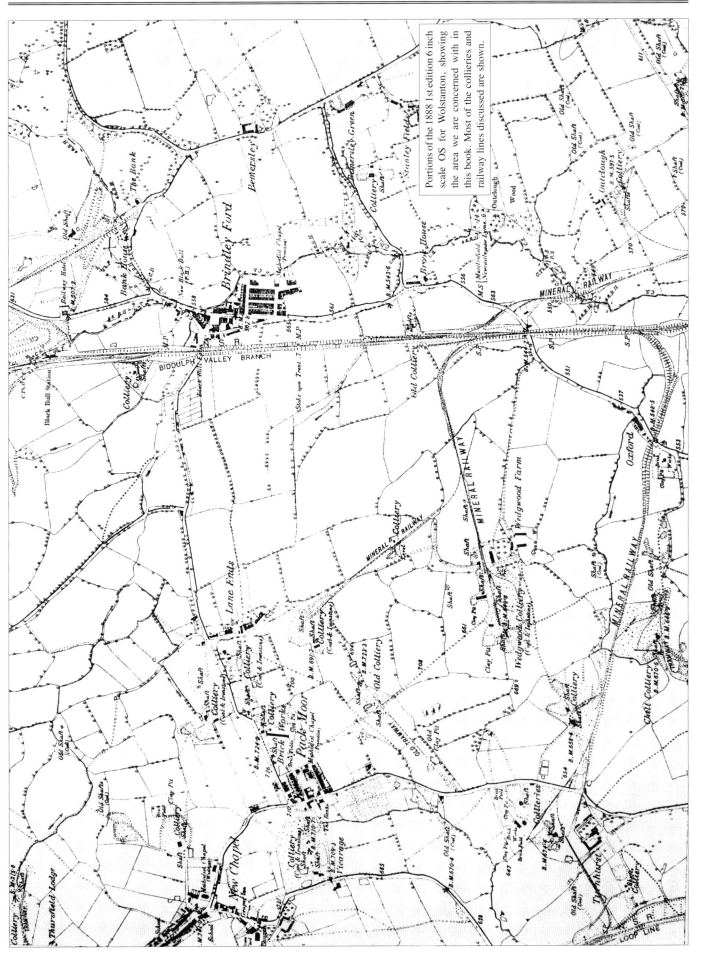

Portions of the 1888 1st edition 6 inch scale OS for Wolstanton, showing the area we are concerned with in this book. Most of the collieries and railway lines discussed are shown.

Anne Henshall at Wolstanton on 8th December 1765 and the couple lived at Turnhurst Hall.[41] Anne was the daughter of John Henshall, a business associate of Brindley.[42] This was at a time when the engineer, his colleagues and business associates (notably the brothers John and Thomas Gilbert), were heavily engaged on the summit section of the Grand Trunk Canal, with its major engineering feat of penetrating Harecastle Hill by a 2,880 yard tunnel. Coal measures having been discovered while driving the tunnel, mining activities in and around Turnhurst became a natural development. In March 1760, John Brindley, a local pottery owner and younger brother of James, along with business associates Hugh Henshall (son of John), Robert Williamson, and John and Thomas Gilbert, purchased the Turnhurst, Newchapel and Goldenhill estates. While James was not directly involved in this transaction, he may have contributed to his brother's share. Whatever the case, James appears to have moved into Turnhurst Hall soon afterwards.[43] The vendor, at least so far as Turnhurst and Newchapel were concerned, was Sir Nigel Gresley 6th Bart (1726-1787), of Apedale in Staffordshire and Drakelow in Derbyshire, who had inherited the estates from his aunt, Anne.[44] Anne was the third of four daughters of Sir William Bowyer 4th Bart (1654-1702), Lord of The Manor of Apedale & Podmore. She married firstly in 1706 Sir John Bellott[45] 4th Bart of Turnhurst Hall and Moreton in Cheshire, who had been Member of Parliament for Newcastle-under-Lyme between 1703 and 1705. On his death (sometime after 1707), she inherited the estates and in surviving her second marriage to Rowe Port of Ilam in Staffordshire, the estates passed to her nephew when she died in 1754, as related above. John Henshall of Newchapel had managed the estates for Anne and would, therefore, have been well aware of their mineral potential.[46]

It is also worth mentioning that as well as the pits described in the following chapters, there were numerous other small and often adjacent mining operations. Very often these were part of the larger undertakings, with the coal and ironstone conveyed by horse and cart to their larger neighbours. However, some would have been quite independent and small, leasing mineral rights from the land owners. It is unlikely any of them sunk shafts to any great depth and some of them may have been drifts as opposed to vertical shafts, always known locally as 'footrails' – pronounced as 'footrills'. Others, even smaller, may have been simple bell pits.[47]

Top: A view of the west or Tunstall end portal of the tunnel on the Whitfield-Pinnox Mineral Railway of Chatterley-Whitfield Collieries. The tunnel was necessary to penetrate the high ground between the Pottery towns and Chell; even so the line had steep gradients on both sides. The photograph was taken on 3rd March 1958. HUGH B. OLIVER

Above: An engraving of Turnhurst Hall and outbuildings dating from 1862. The hall, however, was of much earlier construction; around 1700 is considered to be as accurate an estimate as possible. Until his death in 1772, it was the home of James Brindley.

Right: A much later view of Turnhurst Hall, circa 1922. It was demolished soon after, in 1929.

A view of the Trent & Mersey Canal at Harecastle in about 1910. On the right is the portal of the original Harecastle Tunnel, 2,880 yards long and opened, together with the canal as a through route, in 1777. This canal was to a large extent engineered by James Brindley, although he died in 1772 before it was completed. It was during the boring of the tunnel that Brindley and his partner, John Gilbert, became aware of the extensive coal measures in the area. In fact, all the seams in the North Staffordshire Coalfield can be found in Harecastle Hill. To enable the coal seams to be mined, side canal tunnels were driven from the main waterway, the coal then being loaded directly into the canal boats. On the extreme left, part of the buttressing leading to the portal of the entrance to a second tunnel can be seen. The engineer for this tunnel, completed in March 1827 and 2,926 yards long, was Thomas Telford. It was built to ease traffic congestion, neither tunnel being wide enough for boats to pass; thereafter one tunnel was used for southbound traffic (Brindley's) and the other for northbound. Today, only Telford's tunnel is in use, traffic being controlled on a time

basis. The boat in the centre of the channel, with the Staffordshire Knot motif, is an NSR owned one, doubtless used for maintenance purposes. The Trent & Mersey Canal was acquired by the NSR when the railway company was first incorporated in 1846.

An aerial photograph of Chatterley-Whitfield Colliery in about 1950. As can be seen, this was a large undertaking, with no fewer than five pit shafts on the site. In its heyday, it was the largest single colliery in North Staffordshire. The view is looking due west towards Chell, with the village just off the picture. The new houses to the top right at Fegg Hayes were built in the immediate post war years, largely to house colliery employees and their families.

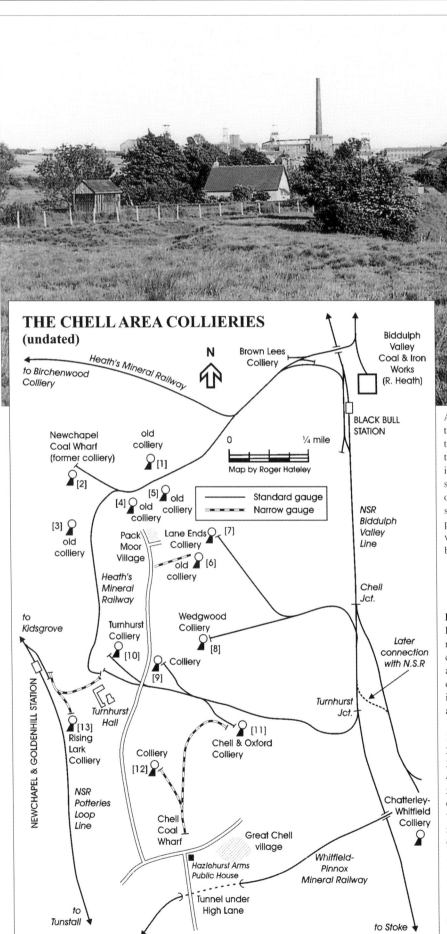

THE CHELL AREA COLLIERIES
(undated)

N

to Birchenwood Colliery

Heath's Mineral Railway

Brown Lees Colliery

Biddulph Valley Coal & Iron Works (R. Heath)

BLACK BULL STATION

Newchapel Coal Wharf (former colliery)

old colliery

[1]

[2]

0   ¼ mile

Map by Roger Hateley

[5] old colliery

[4] old colliery

――――― Standard gauge
━ ━ ━ Narrow gauge

NSR Biddulph Valley Line

[3] old colliery

Pack Moor Village

Lane Ends Colliery [7]

old colliery [6]

Chell Jct.

Heath's Mineral Railway

Wedgwood Colliery

[8]

Later connection with N.S.R

to Kidsgrove

Turnhurst Colliery [10]

Colliery [9]

Turnhurst Jct.

Turnhurst Hall

[13] Rising Lark Colliery

[11]

Chell & Oxford Colliery

Colliery [12]

NSR Potteries Loop Line

NEWCHAPEL & GOLDENHILL STATION

Chell Coal Wharf

Great Chell village

Chatterley-Whitfield Colliery

Hazlehurst Arms Public House

Whitfield-Pinnox Mineral Railway

Tunnel under High Lane

to Tunstall

to Stoke

ABOVE: With Chatterley-Whitfield Colliery in the distance, the former NSR Biddulph Valley line can just be seen to the left, behind the platelayers hut. The embankment to the right centre, with the formation curving to the right in front of the photographer, is the route of the line that served Wedgwood and Lane Ends pits. Notice the width of this, as there was in all probability a passing loop and sidings located at this point, the start of the branch. The photograph, taken about 1970, should also be compared with the view opposite, taken from some distance further back. JOHN HANCOCK

LEFT: The OS map references below all refer to the 1 Inch 7th Series sheet 110, grid square SJ. The numbers relate to those on this map of the Chell Area Collieries, a composite which does not, therefore, present the picture at any particular date. The references without a colliery or pit name are very old workings about which little information has been found and thus no name can be attributed to them:

1	869546	
2	865547	Newchapel
3	865544	
4	867545	
5	874545	Lane Ends
6	873542	
7	874544	Lane Ends
8	872538	Wedgwood
9	869535	
10	866536	Turnhurst
11	874533	Oxford
12	868533	Chell
13	863535	Rising Lark

The sites of these collieries are also marked on the 2.5 Inch 1952 OS map extract to be found on page 60.

IV
WEDGWOOD, LANE ENDS AND BRINDLEY FORD COLLIERIES

Wedgwood and Lane Ends pits are the northernmost of the ones concerning us, while the pit at Brindley Ford need not detain us very much. This colliery was situated alongside the Biddulph Valley line just north of the village of that name and served by a short siding from the main-line. The sidings were later used as a coal landsale wharf operated by Robert Heath & Sons. However, the other two pits were on the high ground around Chell and Wedgwood at least, was in existence by 1859, when it was worked by Hugh Henshall Williamson. Williamson had a number of mining operations in the northern part of North Staffordshire, including the Whitfield Colliery mentioned earlier. He was related to Brindley on his wife's side, which may have been at least one reason why he came by this particular operation. Brindley passed away at Turnhurst Hall on 27th September 1772 and he is buried in nearby Newchapel churchyard. His widow married Robert Williamson in 1775, a local pottery manufacturer and father of Hugh Henshall Williamson.[48]

By December 1872, the operations were in the ownership of Alexander Burnes Anderson (1835-1898) and George Baddeley, with Anderson of Liverpool providing the capital. Baddeley, who gave a Lane Ends, Tunstall address, was a local man and the colliery manager. On 16th December, a new limited liability company was registered, the Wedgwood Coal & Iron Company Ltd, to acquire 'all the estate rights, title and interests' of these two gentlemen, in the 'coal, ironstone and other mines and minerals of the Wedgwood, Lane Ends & Brindley Ford collieries'. The agreement was dated 8th November 1872 and was between the Company, Anderson and Lieutenant-Colonel Percival Robert-Innes (1827-1906).[48A] Anderson was the managing director, holding by far the largest individual number of shares, over 4,000. Unfortunately, we do not know an enormous amount about Robert-Innes although he was, no doubt, a financier of the new undertaking; he held 1,987 shares. Latterly always resident in London, when he died he left an estate of but £1,753. The new company had an enormous capital for the time, bearing in mind the pits were quite small; £200,000 divided in to 20,000 shares of £10. Anderson, who would appear to have been something of an entrepreneur and, by 1861, was practicing as a solicitor in Liverpool, was also a director of the Oak Pits Colliery Company. This company owned the Oak and Bromfield collieries, situated a little to the south west of Mold in Flintshire.[49]

The other directors were Joseph Fry, a director of the Vancouver Coal & Land Company Ltd, with 100 shares, Herbert Sankey of Messrs Sankey Son & Flint of Canterbury, with 125 shares, and Frederic Richards Mealy Gasset, a gentleman of Shoreham in Sussex,

Following on from the previous photograph taken on the same day, this view from further along the line to the Wedgwood and Lane Ends pits again has Chatterley-Whitfield Colliery in the background, in this instance serving also as a useful a reference point between the two pictures. JOHN HANCOCK

with 225 shares. Despite its high level of authorised capital, the Company appears to have been heavily mortgaged. For example, a £60,000 debenture issue at £25 each with an anticipated 10% return, payable in half-yearly instalments over seven years prior to redemption. In addition, there was the possibility of a bonus of 10% after the seven years. The shareholders, however, did not receive any dividend payments unless the debenture interest had been satisfied. By April 1873, the Company had managed to issue no fewer than 15,000 shares, all of which were fully paid-up, of which Anderson held no fewer than 5,740. It cannot thus be said that he did not give sound financial support to the new undertaking, although the Articles did credit him with an annual salary of £2,000 – a large sum in those times. Baddeley, who remained the manager, held only 20 shares. The other directors emoluments consisted of £2 10s per cent per annum, upon the balance of net profits after payment of interest, bonus and annual payments to the debenture holders, along with sufficient to pay the shareholders no less than 12%. This was a tall order and while Anderson appears to have been sitting pretty, his co-directors had a long way to go before any cash came their way! The registered office was initially in London but, from June 1874, was at 12, St. Georges Crescent in Liverpool. The share returns give Anderson's occupation as '*gentleman*'.[49A]

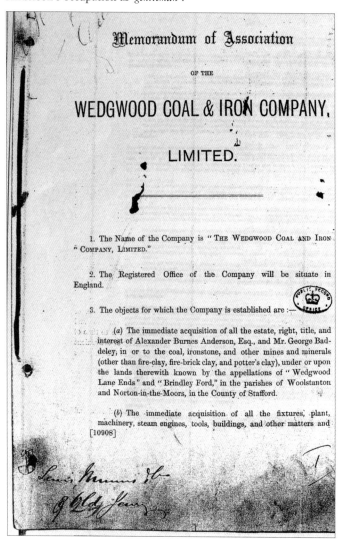

First page of the Memorandum of Association of the Wedgwood Coal & Iron Company Ltd, which was registered on 16th December 1872. NATIONAL ARCHIVES: BT31/1794/6832

The Company held leases for about 350 acres of mineral rights, 270 at Wedgwood and 80 at Lane Ends, with a rent of £400 per year plus Royalties. In the case of ironstone, this was of 11d per ton on the Wedgwood Estate and 1s 6d at Lane Ends; for coal, the figure was 7d on both estates. The difference in the ironstone and coal Royalties illustrates the higher value placed on the ironstone at this period. An abridged report by John Brunton, a London based mining engineer and dated 27th November 1872, accompanied the prospectus for the debenture issue. There were, according to this report, four pits in operation, with another being sunk at Wedgwood, tapping twenty-two coal seams varying in thickness from three to eight feet. This was anticipated to be ready for production in four months. Current output was 200 tons of coal and 160 tons of calcined ironstone per day,[50] with the ironstone presumably being calcined on site prior to sale; it came from the Brown Mine and Burnwood seams. It was estimated the new shaft being sunk would contribute a further 100 tons of coal and 40 tons of calcined ironstone per day. There followed some pretty optimistic financial figures of what might be achieved, along with claims that the mines contained neither gas nor water. The report talks in glowing terms about the thickness of the coal seams and the enormous volumes of ungotten coal and ironstone in the area leased, and the ease with which it was anticipated they could be worked. In fact, the reserves were estimated at a very optimistic 30,000,000 tons of coal and 2,557,427 tons of ironstone, the latter over 117 acres, although the percentage of iron in the stone was not mentioned. All this seems pretty optimistic reading today but a good number of folk accepted it at the time. There were also plans to sink two additional pits, in this case closer to the Biddulph Valley Line of the NSR, to tap the Hardmine and Cockshead coal seams where they were claimed to be 12 feet thick.[51]

Mention of a branch railway to connect with the NSR Biddulph Valley Line is made in the report, quoted as being about one mile long and recently completed. The line was said to be '*equipped with five sets of points and crossings and a good siding*'. Two locomotives were apparently in operation and there was a truck weighing machine, along with workshops to keep locomotives and wagons in working order. Unfortunately, we have no further details of the locomotives but, presumably, as main line access had only recently been established, they would have arrived around the same time – 1872. I cannot imagine they were new and in any event there are no obvious contenders in any manufacturer's lists I have seen so, in all probability, they were second hand. However, see the notes below forming part of the receiver and manager's accounts.

The first annual general meeting of the new company was held on 20th May 1874, at the North Staffordshire Railway Hotel in Stoke with Anderson in the chair, when he painted a very rosy picture of the firm's fortunes. He mentioned that, when the pits were acquired, the product was chiefly ironstone. Responding to criticism from the floor on the amount of ironstone on hand, he made the comparison of 12s 6d a ton when the company was formed and the average price since of 18s 8d a ton. However, while trade had been brisk, the company had suffered from a lack of railway wagons to move the ore to the various south Staffordshire ironworks where most of the trade was located. With the current depression in the trade, only about forty of the 200 or so blast furnaces in the Black Country were in blast. Therefore, production had been concentrated on coal, with the ironstone stock piled until trade picked up. Despite being what he called a young and undeveloped colliery, 60,000 tons of minerals had been mined during the first year which, after deducting costs, left a profit of £12,000. Only a few days ago, 320 tons of coal had been raised and as this was at the end of a drift, it was anticipated that, as the men worked back towards the shaft, up to 2,500 tons a week was a not unreasonable target. The Little Row and Four Foot coal seams had recently been reached in the Brindley Ford part of the estate, claimed to be among the best house coals in the coalfield. As well as George Baddeley, a Mr Clews was also mentioned as a manager – doubtless he would have been the under-manager – both being praised for their unceasing attention, for they had *'scarcely stopped working night and day'*. After the meeting, the assembled company paid a visit to the colliery and were apparently well pleased with what they saw, returning to the hotel afterwards for an *'excellent dinner'*![51A] It would be interesting to know how they travelled from Stoke, a little over five miles by road and, presumably, by horse-drawn carriages. In view of the sparse train service on the NSR Biddulph Valley Line, it is doubtful they would have gone by train, unless a special was chartered.

Whatever the intentions of the Wedgwood Coal & Iron Company Ltd, it did not last very long; at an extraordinary general meeting on 6th August 1875, a resolution was passed for voluntary liquidation, as it was unable, by reason of its liabilities, to continue in business. The Company appointed Harmood Walcot Banner as liquidator, who were also their auditors and of the same address as their own registered office, which was also the address of Anderson's solicitors business! However, there was more to it than this resolution, as the Company was seriously in default in payment of interest on its debenture issue. A gentleman by the name of Richard Brown, on behalf of the holders of first mortgage debentures, petitioned at the Court of Chancery for the appointment of a receiver and manager. The Court met on 19th November 1875, under the direction of vice-chancellor V.C. Malins, when it was ordered that the winding-up should supervised by the Court, Frederick Bertram Smart, a London accountant, being appointed in place of Banner. Smart acted as manager as well as receiver, continuing operation of the colliery from 2nd August 1875 until 30th December 1880. The defendants in the case are quoted as Sir Charles Harbord, Arthur Otway and Matthew Hutton Chaytor, the trustees for the debenture holders. Chaytor was the chairman of the National District Company & Alliance Bank, while Otway was a trustee of the Government & Guaranteed Securities Permanent Trust. Sir Charles Harbord Bart (1830-1914), of Suffield in Norfolk, was the 5th Baron Suffield. He married Cecilia Annetta in May 1854, the youngest daughter of Henry

Baring (1776-1848), one of the principals of the well-established and the oldest London merchant bank of Baring Brothers. This makes it quite possible that Barings Bank may have been involved in underwriting some of the debenture issue. We are fortunate that Smart's accounts have survived, from which the following notes are quite enlightening.[51B]

The accounts show regular payments for coal and ironstone, some quite large amounts paid to individuals, leading to the assumption that the colliery was at least for part of the time, worked on the

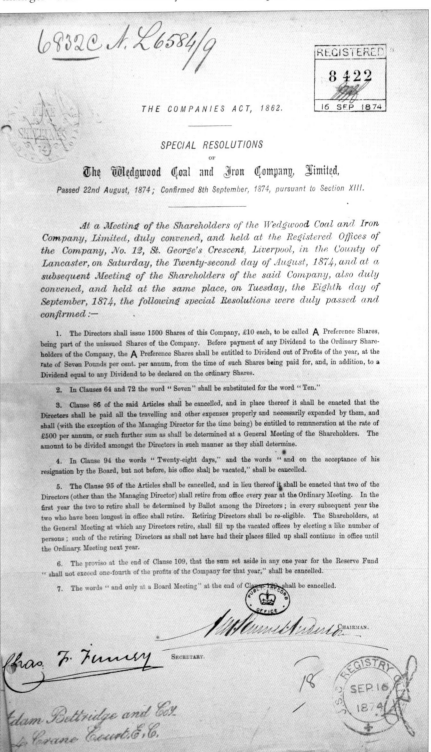

Special Resolution of the Wedgwood Coal & Iron Company Ltd, dated 22nd August 1874, relating to a share issue. Courtesy National Archives: BT31/1794/6832

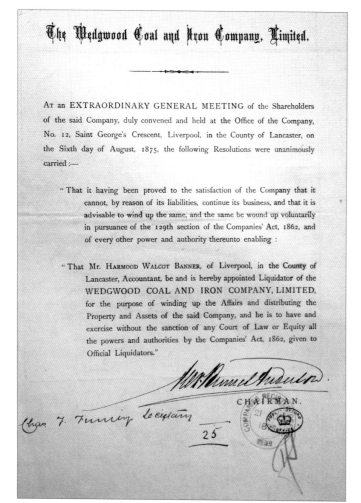

Extraordinary General Meeting resolution of the Wedgwood Coal & Iron Company Ltd, dated 6th August 1875, regarding the appointment of a liquidator. National Archives: BT31/1794/6832

'butty' system. This is where one individual acted as a contractor to the owners, perhaps employing others, to mine coal and ironstone at agreed prices per ton. He would also use his own tools and where employed, pit ponies.[51C] Along with consistent small local coal sales, significant amounts of ironstone went to both north and south Staffordshire ironmasters. The Black Country firms of the New British Iron Company, Noah Hingley & Sons and John Bagnall & Sons were customers, while locally, Earl Granville at Shelton and Etruria, the Goldendale Iron Company, Chatterley Iron Company and J. & A. Glover at Longton were too. A significant customer for coal was the NSR and there were payments to the railway company for coal and ironstone consigned along with siding rent. Royalties were paid for some of the coal raised, for example to the Reverend H. Sutcliffe for his Lane End mines and the Chatterley Iron Company. Railway wagon hire was a constant outlay, largely from the Scottish Wagon Company with, for example, twenty-five wagons on hire for April 1880 at a total cost of £24 11s 8d, while there were fifty-eight wagons on hire in November 1880. Arnold & Garside were also involved, in April 1880 for example, with six wagons hired from them for a period of three months at a cost of £10 10s. Other interesting entries regarding wagons include £26 13s 2d paid by the NSR against a claim that the railway company had detained wagons and £2 16s 6d paid to the NSR for loading wagon No. 44, which had broken down at Crewe.

Regular payments were made to a Mr E Perrins, the manager of the colliery, and Smart in connection with his management. For example, he was paid £1,883 12s 6d on 30th November 1876, covering his fees up to that date. He also claimed expenses, largely travel and subsistence, including trips to the colliery and to attend 'reconstruction meetings' at Stoke, the latter in connection with attempts to get the undertaking out of receivership. On 17th January 1880, an invoice was cleared for £10 10s, described as a survey of the colliery, presumably in connection with a possible sale. There are some interesting entries involving individuals. On 1st January 1879, a Charles Beech was paid £4 2s 9d for coal raised, while on 15th January, a gratuity was paid to his widow following his death. This must have been the result of an underground accident, as the company later settled accounts for medical assistance and a coffin. On 1th April 1880, accounts were settled for the coffin and funeral of J. Hammond, killed in No. 4 pit. There were other not dissimilar cases too.

On 27th March 1877, at an NSR Traffic & Finance Committee meeting, a discussion ensued over plans by the Wedgwood Coal & Iron Company Ltd to work minerals under the Biddulph Valley Line around Black Bull station. The railway company engineer was instructed to ascertain the price of the coal in an area sufficient to protect the line from subsidence. As there is no further mention in the NSR minutes, or the receiver and manager's accounts, we can only assume some sort of agreement was reached

There are some interesting entries regarding locomotives throughout the period of receivership. Quite small sums were paid on a regular basis to both Isaac Gater and H. Baxter, presumably local tradesman undertaking repairs and adjustments. More significant payments were made to Hartley & Arnoux Brothers and Barker & Cope. The partnership of Hartley & Arnoux Brothers, of the California Works at Fenton, dates from 1874, the predecessor of Hartley, Arnoux & Fanning. The works was later acquired by Kerr, Stuart & Company Ltd, a well-known firm of railway locomotive and rolling stock builders. The Hartley Companies had acted as sub-contractors to Kerr, Stuart prior to that company establishing its own manufacturing facilities and there is some evidence that it built and sold locomotives to its own account. It certainly undertook repairs and modifications to local industrial locomotives. It is, therefore, not beyond the bounds of possibility that one or more of the locomotives employed here had been built at the California Works, which might explain why the firm was engaged to undertake repairs. For example, on 10th March 1876, £53 13s was paid and on 16th November 1877, £82 11s 5d, the latter for a locomotive named *Elwy*[51D] and there are earlier and later smaller sums, including one on 21st July 1880 for two '*loco axle boxes*' at £17 10s. The larger sums might suggest that the locomotive was attended to at the California Works. Barker & Cope of Kidsgrove are better known for their stationary engines and other types of plant, although their name often appears in quotes for local industrial locomotive repairs. Another interesting entry covers £1 10s paid on 25th May 1877 to James Lovell, for a '*shed for locomotive*'; in the singular notice, although that might not have any great significance. During the almost six years of receivership, the outlay amounted to £55,796 against an income of £50,709, leaving a deficit of £5,087, after allowing for the receiver & manager's fees.

Exactly what happened next is unclear but the pits would appear to have ceased operation. Be that as it may, there was a second Court of Chancery hearing reported in the *Mining Journal* for 29th

July 1882, in the case of the Wedgwood Coal & Iron Company Ltd and Anne Marie Batten, a shareholder. Resulting from this and according to the *Colliery Guardian* of 11th August 1882, Joseph Cooksey & Son was to sell by auction on 6th September, *'the whole leasehold property of Wedgwood, Lane Ends & Brindley Ford Collieries'* including, *'two locomotive engines'*. In the event, a sale of the colliery equipment did not take place, as we read in the *Colliery Guardian* for 9th February 1883, that Cooksey was to sell, this time by private treaty; the notice included reference to *'locomotive engines, branch railways'* etc. The limited company was not removed from the register of companies until 7th October 1904, following much correspondence between the Registrar of Joint Stock Companies and the various solicitors involved in the winding-up, all denying anything much in the way of responsibility.[52]

According to some existing records of the Birmingham Wagon Company,[53] the Wedgwood Coal & Iron Company Ltd had, between October 1870 and January 1876, hired wagons from them. A total of 185 wagons were hired, most of them from May 1873 to December 1875. The lessor recorded the lessee as successors to *'Baddeley, Taylor & Company of Newchapel'*. We know who Baddeley was from the notes above but the identity of Taylor is a mystery. However, the company may have hired or owned other wagons, as those mentioned above were numbered 10 to 15, 61 to 120 and 122 to 141, leaving a number of gaps. A concern quoted in the wagon company records as being the liquidators of the Company, also hired some wagons from the same lessor but in this case only ten, between February and September 1882. One wonders why; perhaps remaining stocks of coal and or ironstone were being cleared but, if so, it was a long time after mining appears to have ceased – see footnote 66.

Whatever may or may not have happened as a result of Cooksey's actions, we next hear of the pits being worked by Richard Attenborough (1822-1901), trading as the Wedgwood Colliery Company. Attenborough, a native of Northamptonshire, had other mining interests in North Staffordshire, at Hall o' Lee near Scholar Green, as well as several more ironstone mining and engineering activities in various parts of the country. He was declared bankrupt in 1885.[54] Whatever success Attenborough may have had in mining at this location, it appears to have gone unrecorded but operations had ceased again by the early part of 1886. As required by law, the mining plans were deposited with the Home Office on 5th January 1887. On 11th February 1887, the *Colliery Guardian* advertised a sale by Edwards of the plant, *'re Trustees of the Estate*

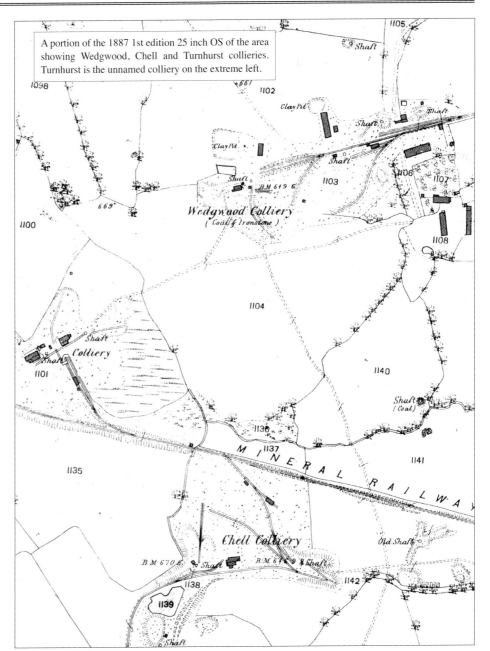

A portion of the 1887 1st edition 25 inch OS of the area showing Wedgwood, Chell and Turnhurst collieries. Turnhurst is the unnamed colliery on the extreme left.

of Richard Attenborough trading as the Wedgwood Colliery Company', which included two locomotives, *'one four coupled and one six coupled'*. These locomotives could of course be the same ones mentioned earlier. Certainly locomotives would have been very useful, as the line serving the pits was steeply graded as it climbed away from the NSR just north of Chell. The junction formed a facing connection for trains heading north and the line was about a quarter of a mile long to serve Wedgwood Colliery. There was also a branch about three furlongs long from its approximate mid-point, to serve the Lane Ends shafts which were to the north, towards Packmoor. The only other reference traced regarding equipment used at these pits is in some surviving records of Hartley, Arnoux & Fanning, the Fenton-based mechanical engineers mentioned above, regarding a possible supply of pit tubs in June 1883. The company certainly quoted, although whether any were supplied has gone unrecorded.[55]

Although we have no definite date when the junction was made between the branch and the main line, the NSR minutes being silent on the matter, we do know of another siding at almost the same

This view, taken on 20th April 1976, is looking north along the Biddulph Valley from the siding connection for Chatterley-Whitfield Colliery, which was controlled by the ground frame on the left. This particular connection dated from April 1964, when the private line to Pinnox Sidings at Tunstall closed, after which all colliery rail traffic went via the Biddulph Valley Line. Although on the approximate site of the earlier sidings for both Chatterley-Whitfield and the Turnhurst and Chell Branch, the Chatterley-Whitfield connection was on the opposite side of the line, with the site of that for Turnhurst and Chell being behind the photographer. The level ground at the base of the Brown Lees Colliery dirt tip, in the upper left distance, is the formation of the route to the Wedgwood and Lane Ends pits. Victoria Colliery, at Black Bull, can just be discerned in the middle distance. The underbridge seen here at the toe end of the rail connection took the Chell to Biddulph road under the railway.

location. Hugh Henshall and Edward Williamson were in contact with the NSR, variously between November 1860 and November 1861, regarding siding connections for their traffic on the Biddulph Valley Line.[56] As well as the Wedgwood and Lane End pits, the Williamsons were at this time, as mentioned earlier, operating Whitfield Colliery. The brothers also worked the Brown Lees pit at Black Bull, which was later part of the Robert Heath Estate. A November 1860 minute of the NSR Traffic Committee, specifically refers to a connection with the main line to serve Brown Lees Colliery, which was agreed. Later minutes, however, make no specific mention of which siding was in question, just that it was on the Biddulph Valley Line. The connections for Whitfield Colliery and the later line to serve the Wedgwood and Lane End pits, were almost directly opposite each other. It may be, therefore, that a separate siding agreement was not felt necessary. The issue with the Williamson brothers would not appear to have been a straightforward one, as on two occasions the brothers attended the committee in person to elucidate exactly what they wanted, although unfortunately the minutes do not help us understand exactly what the issues were. It was not until 5th November 1861 that the agreement was signed. It is possible that the siding connections for the Wedgwood and Lane End Branch could have been worked by the same signal box as those for Whitfield Colliery and this may be why a specific mention was not made by the NSR directors in their deliberations. The line would

have been lifted soon after the pits closed and its route is shown as a former railway on the 1900[57] 6-inch Ordnance Survey map of the area.[58] When I last trudged the area some forty odd years ago, parts of the course of the branch could still be traced, including sections of a cutting as it climbed onto the higher ground.[59]

There is some evidence that, around 1891, Robert Heath & Sons, at that time operating the adjacent Newchapel Colliery, may have also reopened a shaft or shafts at Lane Ends for the extraction of ironstone. This being the case, either the ironstone would have been transported to Newchapel Colliery by horse and cart, or it may be a siding was built to connect Lane Ends with a line Heath's built to serve Newchapel Colliery, forming a connection with the ironworks and collieries at Black Bull. This is covered in more detail in Chapter V11.

Attenborough's Hall o' Lee Colliery Company was also in liquidation and the *Colliery Guardian* advertised a sale of plant there, including a locomotive, to be held on 16th-17th September 1886. As in the case of the two locomotives at Wedgwood Colliery, this one has not been identified, although circumstantial evidence would suggest it was narrow gauge, while the other two were standard gauge. The railways at Hall o' Lee were almost certainly narrow gauge, feeding the Macclesfield Canal rather than the main line railway. So far as is known, there was no main line railway connection with that pit.

V

THE TURNHURST HALL
COAL & IRONSTONE COMPANY

This was an early operator of the pits at Turnhurst along with another quite small pit, the Rising Lark, located on the Goldenhill side of the ridge of high ground alongside the NSR Potteries Loop Line, just to the south of Goldenhill station.[60] There was a narrow gauge and probably rope-hauled tramway between Turnhurst and the NSR sidings at Goldenhill, with a short branch serving the Rising Lark pit.[61] The line from Turnhurst to the NSR loading platforms at Goldenhill was approximately 250 yards long. It probably operated from as early as 1863. On 6th April 1875, the NSR Traffic & Finance Committe (T&FC) considered a request by the Turnhurst Colliery Company to lay down a tramway across the mine loading stage at Goldenhill station. This was agreed at an annual payment of £1, along with an agreement to remove the tramway if so requested at three months notice. On 15th August 1876, the NSR considered a request to extend the sidings at Goldenhill and the company's engineer was authorised to accept a payment from the Turnhurst Colliery Company of £100 for the work.[62] The colliery closed for the first time in 1879 but the plant was not auctioned until July 1886. The *Colliery Guardian*, in its issue dated 16th July 1886, contains an advert of which the following is an extract: '*A.T. Crow to auction 28 July 1886 plant on dismantlement of Turnhurst Collieries Golden Hill* [sic] *near Stoke, including four-wheels coupled tank locomotive, also Aveling & Porter locomotive engine with drum gear.*' Unfortunately, neither of these machines has been positively identified, although as it could be assumed that the four wheels coupled tank engine was standard gauge, this might refer to the locomotive *Norah*, mentioned below.

Details of the sale in the *Birmingham Post* give additional information. Among the plant was a high pressure beam pumping engine with a cylinder 22ins x 48ins and a heavy flywheel, along with four winding engines indicating that there were, perhaps, four shafts in use at the time of closure. The winding engines consisted of a single cylinder engine with a cylinder 22ins x 48ins, fitted with Cornish valves, another, a twin cylinder engine with cylinders 16ins x 36ins, a third with twin cylinders 15ins x 26ins, along with a 7ft diameter drum which was 5ft wide, and lastly, a single cylinder engine with cylinders 16ins x 30ins. This last one had been made by Scragg of Congleton. There were several other engines driving pumps etc., along with eight boilers, five of Lancashire design 36ft long by 5ft 6ins diameter and three egg ended 38ft long and 6ft diameter. Particularly interesting is a reference to an incline hauling engine with cylinders 12ins x 24ins, equipped with treble haulage gear and a rope drum 9ft in diameter and 7ft wide, along with a horizontal drum and gear. A reasonable assumption is that this equipment was used in association with the narrow gauge incline from the colliery to the NSR at Goldenhilll, perhaps confirming that this was in fact a rope-hauled incline. On the other hand, I suppose it could have been used for haulage underground with steam supplied from the boiler plant on the surface. However, the size of the drum – 9ft in diameter – would suggest to me that this would be unlikely. Also included in the sale was a 17 ton weighbridge and fifty-one standard gauge 8-ton railway wagons made by the Midland Company. This would be the Midland Railway Carriage & Wagon Company Ltd, with works at Saltley in Birmingham and in Shrewsbury.[63]

In January 1993, during opencast coal mining on the site of the former Robert Heath & Sons Ltd[64] pit at Brown Lees, only a mile or so north east from Turnhurst, the remains of an Aveling & Porter tramway type locomotive were discovered.[65] The description of the Aveling & Porter engine in the *Colliery Guardian* advert quoted above, with the mention of drum gear, would lead one to believe that the locomotive had been converted for use as a stationary haulage engine. This leads to the assumption that the Turnhurst engine was sold at the auction, moved to Brown Lees and, perhaps, used there as an underground haulage engine. If this was the case, then in all probability the boiler would not have been used, steam being piped into the pit from boilers situated above ground. These remains have survived, initially at the Chatterley-Whitfield Mining Museum but currently in the custody of David Viewing of Welton

Two photographs of the remains of the Aveling & Porter traction engine type geared and chain driven locomotive mentioned above. This is almost exactly as the remains were discovered when opencast mining took place on the site of Brown Lees Colliery in January 1993. The engine is owned by David Viewing and located in Northamptonshire. BOB DARVILL

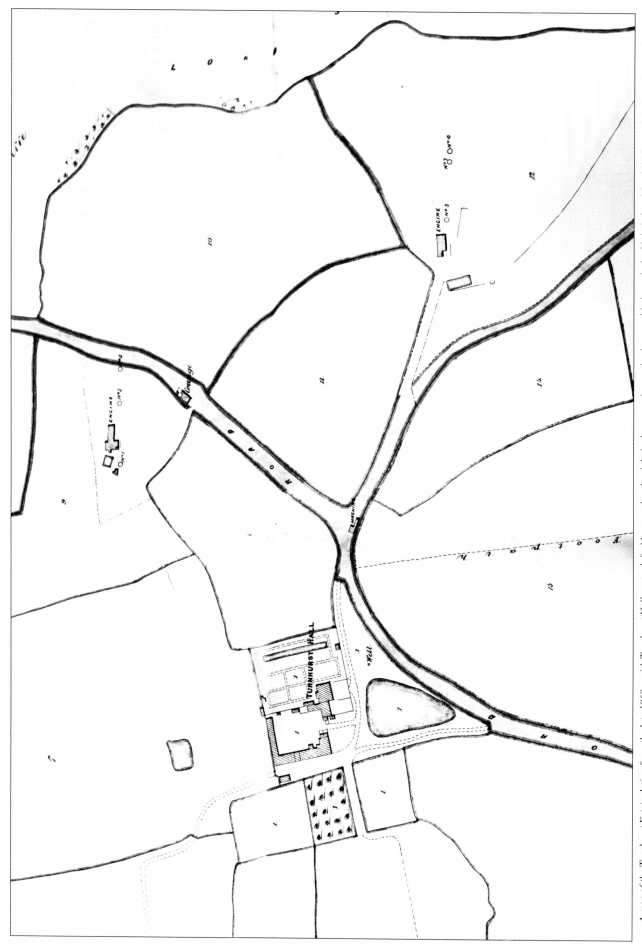

A map of the Turnhurst Estate dating from the late 1860s, with Turnhurst Hall centre left. Above and to the right is shown a mine engine house with three shafts, No's 1, 2 and 5, whilst lower right is another engine house with three more shafts, No's 3, 4 and 7. The original plan is hand coloured, with the rectangle adjacent to this second engine being coloured blue, indicating that it was most likely a reservoir providing water for this engine; a similar smaller blue rectangle exists behind the engine house at the top. South of Turnhurst Hall is a large triangular lake or pond that is also coloured blue and note the Machine shown at the road junction in the centre of the map. F.J. Hazlehurst owned the mineral rights to the south of the estate, off the bottom of the portion of the map show here. STAFFORDSHIRE COUNTY RECORD OFFICE: D3272/1/10/5/17

in Northamptonshire. The surviving parts consist of a section of the boiler with the engine mounted on top, from which a cylinder size of 10ins x 12ins has been established. This identifies the locomotive as one of the builder's 10 horsepower machines, of which there are few contenders of the right vintage, the histories of which are otherwise unrecorded.[66] From the possible contenders I am inclined to the view that the engine in question is Aveling & Porter No. 235 which, according to surviving records of the maker, was supplied in October 1866 to W. Brassey & Lucas.[67] This has to be a reference to Thomas Brassey and the Lucas Brothers, both well established railway contractors. However, as far as I am aware, no contracts are known where these two contractors worked together without any other partner.[68] The late David Cole, in his *Contractors Locomotives Part One* (Union Publications 1964), tells us that Thomas Brassey, in partnership with William Field, built the GWR line from Corwen to Bala in 1864 and two of the Aveling & Porter locomotives were used on that job. Lawrence Popplewell, in his *A Gazetteer of the Railway Contractors of Wales & The Borders* (Melledgen Press 1984), expands somewhat on this. In this book we learn that the same partners built the line from Llangollen to Corwen in the period 1861 to 1865, followed by the line onwards to Bala which opened on 1st April 1868. Thomas Brassey was the contractor who built the NSR line from Silverdale to Market Drayton, in the period from 1866 until it opened on 1st February 1870. This contract had actually been let to his erstwhile partner, William Field, who sub-let it to Brassey. It would appear quite likely that Brassey used the Aveling & Porter locomotive on this contract, subsequently offering it for sale on completion of the works when it migrated to Turnhurst.[69] On the face of it, this was a machine far from ideal for the steeply graded Turnhurst Branch but these Aveling & Porter locomotives were chain driven and had a high ratio between engine and track speeds, which enabled them to shift quite significant loads, albeit at a very slow speed. Alternatively, it might have been confined to shunting around the colliery yard or used as a stationary winding engine, although in this case above ground. The sale description would certainly suggest its use was of a stationary nature, at least latterly.

On 25th January 1887, C.J. Homer entered into an agreement with Martha Napier, of Alderley Edge in Cheshire and described as a widow, along with Mary Walker, the wife of Rev'd James Harold Walker of Weston Coyney, as owners in equal shares to purchase part of the Turnhurst Estate. This included mineral rights of a little over 110 acres.[70] Charles James Horatio Homer (1837-1893) was a prominent North Staffordshire mining engineer and entrepreneur, inheriting property in Hanley on the death of a relative in 1864. Subsequently, he speculated successfully into a number of areas, not least mining, and became a rich man with a lot of property. A founder member of the North Staffordshire Institution of Mining Engineers and its president in 1874-1876, in 1864 he became the managing director and mining engineer of the Chatterley Iron Company.[71] In developing and expanding the activities of this company, in 1872 he was responsible for the acquisition by the Chatterley Company of Whitfield Colliery at Fegg Hayes.[72] At that time the colliery was working minerals in areas where Homer owned significant mineral rights. He was also involved in the conception and construction of the Longton, Adderley Green & Bucknall Railway, a line built to serve an area to the south east of Stoke-upon-Trent, a district not otherwise covered by the NSR. It penetrated land where he owned considerable property and where he was already engaged in developing the extraction of minerals. This railway, which opened in September 1875, was always worked by the NSR and absorbed by that company in January 1895. Homer was also heavily involved in the Stafford Colliery & Ironworks at Great Fenton, as well as unsuccessful

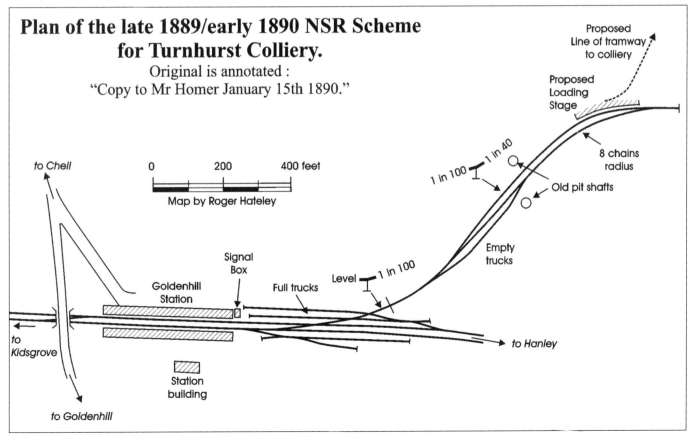

Plan of the late 1889/early 1890 NSR Scheme for Turnhurst Colliery.

Original is annotated :
"Copy to Mr Homer January 15th 1890."

A postcard view of Goldenhill station, looking east circa 1905, with the single-storey main station building on the right and the station master's house (which still survives) on the left. On the left is the Goldenhill to Chell road and Newchapel church is visible on the skyline just left of centre. The smoking chimney marks the site of Robert Heath's Brown Lees Colliery. BASIL JEUDA COLLECTION

attempts, in the period 1888 to 1892, to salvage something out of the collapse of the Kinnersly Ironworks and mining activities on the Clough Hall Estate at Kidsgrove. In the event, it was Robert Heath & Sons Ltd that was able to make something out of the Clough Hall Estate, later building a private mineral line to connect Black Bull with Clough Hall; this line features in Chapter VII.

On 31th December 1889, the NSR T&FC agreed to the provision of a new siding connection on the Loop Line at Goldenhill for Turnhurst Colliery, the sum of £225 being paid by Mr Homer. By this time, Homer had reopened one or both of the Turnhurst and Rising Lark collieries but for how long the operations lasted has gone unrecorded. Homer died on 4th November 1893 but his executors, consisting of Mary Anne Miller (formerly Keyon) and William Adams Cowlishaw, appear to have continued to operate the colliery, or collieries, until around the middle of the 1890s.[73] In September

1899, T.F. Hazlehurst, who we shall hear much of later in this narrative, was in discussions with Chatterley-Whitfield Collieries regarding the Oxford mines, part of Homer's estate, controlled by his executors and sub-leased from Chatterley-Whitfield as the head lessee. Hazlehurst worked these mines in conjunction with Chell and Turnhurst, and he was enquiring about sub-leasing to a new company about to be formed.[74] The new company, the Tunstall Coal & Iron Company Ltd, formed in 1900 and the subject of the next chapter, was proposing to reopen Turnhurst. This prompted Chatterley-Whitfield to have a detailed inspection of the mines it leased from Homer's executors and, in doing so, a number of encroachments

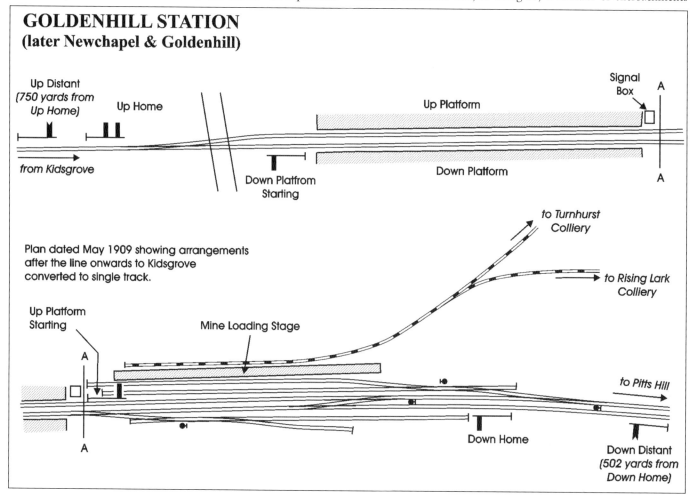

GOLDENHILL STATION
(later Newchapel & Goldenhill)

Newchapel & Goldenhill station was situated on the Potteries Loop Line. This view, taken on 12 April 1962, shows the sidings on both the Up and Down sides. The station was not particularly well situated for either of the villages it served, being at the bottom of a shallow valley and almost equi-distant from both, and always struggled for passengers as a result. The main station building, a single-storey, brick-built structure with later extension and boasting three chimneys, had been sited at the far end of the brick wall at the rear of the platform on the right; it can be seen in the circa 1905 view opposite and had clearly been demolished some years before the passenger service ended. The edge of this platfrom is all that remains of the station today and the route here is now a cycle and footpath. F.W. SHUTTLEWORTH

Another view of Newchapel & Goldenhill station, looking south with the 4.18pm Macclesfield to Wolverhampton DMU arriving on 28th September 1963. The wagons in the siding beyond the signal box stand at the former mine loading stage for the Turnhurst and Rising Lark collieries. Turnhurst Colliery was on the hill to the left, roughly by the top of the signal post. The chimney, top centre, marks the site of Westcliffe Hospital, the former workhouse. MICHAEL MENSING

were discovered into the Oxford Estate. It was estimated that this had taken place between 1887 and October 1899, the date of the inspection. Hazlehurst's defence was that this must have taken place prior to his sub-lease, which was dated 1st March 1898. It then transpired that Beswick, Hazlehurst's manager of the colliery, was aware of the encroachments and when he attended a meeting of the Chatterley-Whitfield Colliery officials on 1st November, he accepted that Hazlehurst would have to pay an estimated Royalty on the coal and ironstone got. It was the Twist coal that had been illegally worked and the issue dragged on into the regime of the new Tunstall Coal & Iron Company. However, it is perhaps best to conclude the issue at this point, before moving on to the history of the new company.

Obstacles were placed in the way of J.W. Byrne, a surveyor on behalf of Chatterley-Whitfield, going underground to make a detailed inspection. Solicitors became involved representing both parties and it was not until November 1900, when accompanied by Richard Steel, Hazlehurst's mining surveyor, that Byrne made his inspection. He established that as well as the ill-gotten coal taken since Hazlehurst had been involved, there were earlier encroachments in the period when Beswick had been working the mines under his own banner. At this point, F.S. Dale, Homer's executors' surveyor, also got involved, his view being that as the mines in question only came into Hazlehurst's control as a result of a lawsuit in October

1885, there was doubt that anybody could be held responsible for mines gotten illegally prior to that date. He went on to say that the new Tunstall Coal & Iron Company should be requested to reopen some of the workings that had already been closed, so as to establish just how much coal and ironstone had been extracted without permission. A formal application on these lines followed on 6th February 1901, asking the new company to reopen the old workings. At the same time, as a director of the new company, Hazlehurst was requested to assist as much as he could. Not surprisingly, while Hazlehurst expressed his willingness to pay any Royalties due for encroachments during the time of his lease, the Tunstall Company declined to reopen the workings unless he, Hazlehurst, paid any costs involved. The matter continued to drag on with numerous meetings of the individuals concerned, Hazlehurst making various offers of compensation, while continuing to refuse to consider any liability for mines got illegally prior to his lease. The question of reopening the old workings, long since stopped-off, held little or no prospect. Eventually, an agreement was reached with Hazlehurst paying a Royalty of £360 for the Twist coal and £234 for ironstone, which appears to have closed the matter.[75] Relations between Chatterley-Whitfield and Hazlehurst, however, remained on cordial terms. The agreement allowed for part of the financial settlement to be in lieu of future Royalties otherwise payable to him, on coal and ironstone mined on parts of his estate that were leased to the colliery company.

VI

THE TUNSTALL COAL & IRON COMPANY LTD AND ITS PREDECESSORS

The Tunstall Coal & Iron Company Ltd was formed in May 1900, to acquire the Chell, Turnhurst and Oxford collieries, although it would appear that Turnhurst had not been worked for some time prior to this date. The prospectus tells us that Chell Colliery belonged to Thomas Francis Hazlehurst, who had recently acquired Turnhurst Colliery.[76] Robert Beswick had worked the Chell and Oxford pits earlier and is named as so doing in the published *Mineral Statistics for Oxford Colliery* from 1854 to 1860. Certainly, until these pits closed, they were known locally as Beswick's Pits.

RIGHT: Thomas Francis Hazlehurst, a portrait taken circa 1912.

BELOW: A Tunstall Coal & Iron Company Ltd ornate letter heading. The letter, dated 6th February 1901, is addressed to the Stock Exchange and while it infers the company's first annual return would be for the year ending 30th June, in the event it was to 31st March. LONDON METROPOLITAN ARCHIVES: GUILD HALL LIBRARY STOCK EXCHANGE ANNUAL COMPANY REPORTS

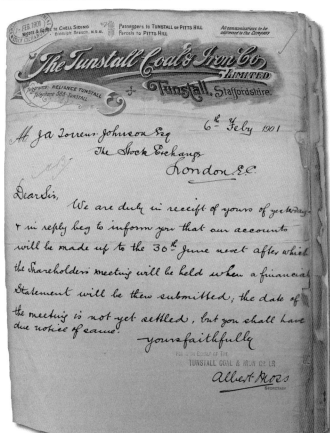

Robert Beswick was born in about 1804 at Hilliwell near Bolton in Lancashire. By 1841, he had arrived in North Staffordshire, married a local girl of about the same age, Rachael, and was resident at Watergate Street in Tunstall.[77] In 1851, he was working coal and ironstone at Chell under the title of the Chell Coal & Iron Company. He also traded as a brick and tile manufacturer, the Dale Hall Brick & Tile Company, with works at Ellgrave Street in Burslem, and as an earthenware manufacturer he owned a pottery, the Church Bank Works in Tunstall.[78] This was in his ownership by 1841.[79]

On 24th January 1865, Thomas Francis Hazlehurst of Cold Ashby Hall at Rugby, who we met briefly in the last chapter, entered into an agreement with the NSR to form a siding connection, to be known as Turnhurst Sidings, on the Biddulph Valley Line, just to the south of where the road from Chell to Biddulph went under the railway. The agreement refers to a branch railway then being built by Messrs Bankhart and this is the standard gauge line built to serve the pits at both Chell and Turnhurst, which formed a junction with the NSR facing towards Congleton.[80] This is interesting, as it would appear from the terrain of the land to have been just as easy for the junction to have faced the opposite way. It is, however, perhaps indicative that the coal and, more importantly, ironstone would be destined to go north for Robert Heath's new ironworks at Black Bull.

Hazlehurst inherited much of the land and property he owned at Chell and the surrounding area on the death of his first wife, Maria Lokier Hazlehurst (née Kirkham) in January 1863.[81] The marriage had taken place at Edgbaston on 15th August 1857, when Hazlehurst was said to be resident at Sandiwdy Lodge,[82] which is near Cuddington in Cheshire. His bride, who was born in 1821, was the widow of Thomas Kirkham of Trent Vale in Stoke-upon-Trent and the daughter of the late A. Parker of Broadwell Hall at Oldbury in Shropshire, so quite why the event took place at Edgbaston is a mystery. Maria had inherited the land from her first husband, Thomas Kirkham, one of the principal land owners at both Great and Little Chell. Hazlehurst married secondly on 29th August 1867, at Richmond in Surrey, to Blanche Devereux. She was born in 1846, the youngest daughter of Robert, 15th Viscount Hereford. Thomas Hazlehust himself was born in 1830, the only son of John Hazlehurst (1803-1885), who traded as a soap manufacturer at Runcorn in Cheshire. By 1895, Hazlehurst was deputy lieutenant of Leicestershire and a JP in both that county and Northamptonshire.[83] His involvement in North Staffordshire, however, fluctuated between helping to develop the estates by financing a railway connection, leasing his minerals to others or, in some cases, a more direct involvement either in partnerships or as was resident locally at Fegg Hayes. Both brothers are mentioned in an April 1874 mortgage agreement as coal owners, formerly copper smelters of Briton Ferry. Presumably, therefore, by this date they had disposed of their South Wales interests. I have no idea what brought the Bankharts to North Staffordshire and they were not around for very long. Whatever it was, it cannot have been copper. Between November 1870 and April 1872, Frederick & Howard Bankhart leased twelve wagons, their fleet numbers 21 to 33, from the Birmingham Wagon Company (*see footnote 53*).

Bowers, in partnership with William Challinor, an earthenware manufacturer of High Street in Fenton[86], purchased part of the Turnhurst estate in September 1853 from William Beaumont. In July 1859 they added to the estate with the purchase of additional land from John Piggot Worthington, while in January 1861 Bowers bought out the interest of the Challinor family - by this time William, Edward and William (the younger). To fund the acquisition to the tune of £16,000, which would seem to have been at least the larger

a shareholder in a limited company. He never seems to have resided in the area, always giving addresses at Rugby, in Leicestershire or in Cheshire.

In any event, Beswick remained involved in the Chell operation for many more years, either as a partner with Hazlehurst and others, or as manager. Legend has it that Hazlehurst mentioned to several people that Bankhart and G.F. Bowers were in possession of part of the Chell and Turnhurst properties before he became involved and, having run short of cash, were willing to sell.[84] George Frederick Bowers, of the Brownhills China Works at Tunstall, conveyed his interests in the Turnhurst Estate to the two Bankhart brothers in September 1863.[85] At that time, the brothers were quoted as being copper smelters and while Frederick Bankhart gave a Lombard Street, London address, his brother, Howard, resided at Briton Ferry in Glamorgan, where they were involved with the Red Jacket and Jersey Marine copper works. The Jersey Marine activity was later part of the Cape Copper Company Ltd, which had operations at Briton Ferry, as well as in India and South Africa. By April 1874, while brother Frederick still lived in the south, at Hendon, Howard

ABOVE: A Turnhurst Colliery & Ironstone Works letter dated 24th August 1861, regarding a mortgage. It is signed by George Frederick Bowers, who is referred to in the text. STAFFORDSHIRE COUNTY RECORD OFFICE: D3272/1/10/5/17

RIGHT: First page of the agreement dated 24th January 1865, between the NSR and Thomas Francis Hazlehurst regarding the Turnhurst Branch Railway and its connection with the Biddulph Valley line. Notice reference to the branch railway being constructed by Messrs Bankhart and T.F. Hazlehurst. NATIONAL ARCHIVES: RAIL 532/175

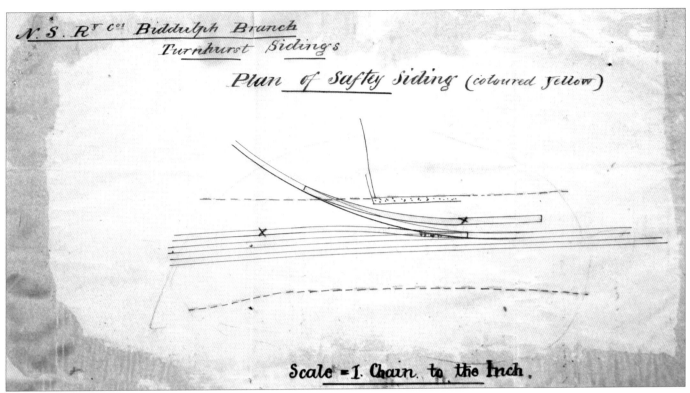

The 1865 NSR plan of the safety siding (marked by the 'X' on the right) referred to in the text, at Turnhurst Sidings on the Biddulph Valley line, where the Turnhurst Branch Railway left the mainline. NATIONAL ARCHIVES: RAIL 532/175

part of the agreed price, if not all of it, a mortgage was arranged. When Bowers sold on to the Bankharts in September 1863, this mortgage was transferred and the financial commitment with mounting interest became a millstone round the necks, not only of the Bankharts, but others later involved in the estate. Bowers by the way, was at one period also in partnership with members of the Challinor family at yet more pottery manufactories at Brownhills, as well as elsewhere in the area[87].

The Turnhurst Hall Colliery & Ironstone Company Ltd may have been registered sometime early in 1863.[88] Its prospectus outlined the proposed capital as £75,000, in 15,000 shares of £5 each, being offered for public subscription.[89] The directors were quoted as Frederick Bankhart; John Braithwaite Honham of Tottenham; Richard Blackhurst, the chief bailiff of Tunstall; Thomas Cooper, a London-based barrister; G.F. Bowers of Brownhills; and Charles Lean, late of the Cwm Avon Iron Works and doubtless a colleague of the Bankharts. The mineral estate consisted of 110 acres and there were no less than sixteen shafts, doubtless an indication of earlier shallow operations, of which four were in use. At the time of the prospectus, some of these shafts were being sunk lower to reach the Burnwood ironstone and the Twist coal,[90] and it was anticipated that, within four months, 1,000 tons a week would be raised for which there was a ready market. According to the consulting engineers, Messrs Woodhouse & Jeffcock of Derby, a dividend of 10% could easily be achieved and if new shafts were sunk near the western boundary, the minerals could be got more easily. This, it was suggested, would mean around 2,500 tons per week being raised and the dividend raised to 15% – all of which sounds very grand! There was mention that arrangements had been made with the NSR and the owner of the intervening land, to construct a branch railway, which it was claimed would result in a saving in carriage of over 1s (5p) per ton, or 5% on a get of 1,000 tons per week. A provisional agreement had

been reached with the owner of the minerals to take one third of the share capital in lieu of any purchase price or Royalties.

As early as 11th March 1863, the company had requested the NSR to provide a siding connection at Chell but it would appear to have been left to Hazlehurst to foot the bill. The NSR costs amounted to little over £975, which included widening the embankment. A safety siding was later added to the estimates at an additional cost of £100. The NSR, in typical fashion, rounded this up to £1,100, Hazlehurst being liable to pay 6% per annum on the outlay over a period of twenty-one years from the end of March 1865. The agreement was signed on 24th January, which would seem to be when the works were completed.[91] The line was very steep for its entire length and by the time it crossed the Chell to Biddulph road – a little less than a quarter of a mile into its route, the road being about 10 feet lower than the railway – the height was sufficient to clear a double deck bus. I can personally testify to this, as the remains of the masonry supports lasted for many years after the line passed out of use. The one on the Chell side of the road looked rather incongruous, as the embankment had been removed to make way for a housing estate. The distance from the junction to Turnhurst was almost a mile, with Chell Colliery situated about half way. One presumes the later decision to include a safety siding at the junction was to protect the NSR sidings from any runaways.[92] From such documentary evidence as we have, the Bankharts appear to have started to build the branch railway to serve both the Chell and Turnhurst properties, while it was left to Hazlehurst to complete the works.[93] Certainly the latter was involved in the negotiations with the NSR for the connection with the Biddulph Valley line. Both the Bankharts and Hazlehurst realised the value of having direct rail access. In February 1874, the company purchased ten wagons from the Birmingham Wagon Company, numbered 81 to 90, and in November 1879, hired another twenty from the same source, numbers 91 to 110. In December 1881, the second lot were purchased (*see footnote 53*).

There is a Hazlehurst Arms public house at Chell, to remind one of times past, although in earlier times it was known as Brindley's Arms. On 1st May 1867, Hazlehurst entered into an agreement with John Thornhill Gibson, a blacksmith, to lease a public house, the Brindley Arms at Chell, along with an adjacent blacksmiths shop, for thirteen years at a rent of £36 per annum. The 1876-1878 OS map of the area shows a public house called Brindley's Arms, while later surveys show the same building as the Hazlehurst Arms. Doubtless at some point in time Hazlehurst had the name changed to reflect his ownership.[94]

Before proceeding further, two other companies, both registered with limited liability under the various Companies Acts, have to be explored. On 30th October 1874, the Chell Coal & Iron Company Ltd was registered. The objects of this company included: *'The immediate acquisition of all estate, right, title, and interest of Robert Beswick, in or to the coal, ironstone, fire clay, fire brick clay, potters clay, and other*

mines and minerals under or upon the lands known by the appellation of the Chell Collieries, situate in the Parish of Wolstanton in the County of Stafford.' An agreement, dated 27th October 1874, had been entered into between William Marshall and Henry Gardner on behalf of the new company, with Robert Beswick as the current owner of the estate rights, title and property, etc. The capital of the new company was the rather large sum of £120,000, which was divided into 12,000 shares of £10 each; the purchase price was £65,000. The first 10,000 shares were intended to be issued (although there is no evidence that they actually were) as fully paid-up to the various people who were involved, including those listed below. The first manager was Robert Beswick junior (1840-1913)[95] and the first secretary Henry Gardner. The initial directors along with Beswick were Thomas Birch Hall, John Edward Hawkes, Robert Haldenby Keyworth, James Perry Senior and Charles Trotter. Notice that neither Marshall, recorded as a gentleman with no occupation and living in Bayswater (London), or Gardner, similarly a gentleman with no occupation and an address of 14 St. George Chambers, Lord Street in Liverpool, were directors. The new company was Liverpool-based, with offices at 10 Cumberland Street. The mineral area consisted of 83 acres held under a thirty year lease, at a rent of £300 per acre plus Royalties, which equated to 1d per ton. It was estimated the amount of coal available was unlimited, the thickness of the seam 80 feet at a depth of 860 yards. The ironstone in the Rusty Mine, New and Burnwood seams was claimed to contain 54% iron, which would appear to be highly optimistic. The weekly output was estimated at 2,000 tons of coal and ironstone, with a conservative view that this would return a profit of £25,000 to £30,000 per annum. In the prospectus the property, plant and machinery, perhaps optimistically, was valued at £150,000 and it was intended to secure 1,600 debentures of £50 each against this. What if anything the company achieved has not been established but it cannot have amounted to very much. In August 1878, the Registrar of Joint Stock Companies was writing to the Liverpool address as the statutory returns had not been submitted; the letter was returned marked *'Not to be found'*. Several other letters to various solicitors in Liverpool over the next few years brought similar responses and the company was struck off the Register on 17th July 1885. It would seem that a number of wealthy gentlemen had been persuaded by Robert Beswick to form a company and in effect, buy out the bulk of his interests, although retaining him as manager. However, whether in fact anything very much took place under this new company's auspices remains a mystery.[96]

The second company was formed almost coincident with the one above. Robert Beswick & Company Ltd was registered on 23rd February 1875 to, inter alia, *'acquire the estate, rights, title and interest of Robert Beswick in the estate known as Chell Collieries.'* In this case, the capital was £100,000 divided into 10,000 shares of £10 each and the registered office was at Chell Colliery. The formation of this company followed an agreement between Robert Beswick and Luke Bishop[97] dated 1st February 1875, whereby for the sum of £60,000, *'Bishop*

First page of the Memorandum of Association of the Chell Coal & Iron Company Ltd, registered on 30th October 1874. NATIONAL ARCHIVES: BT31/2040/8876

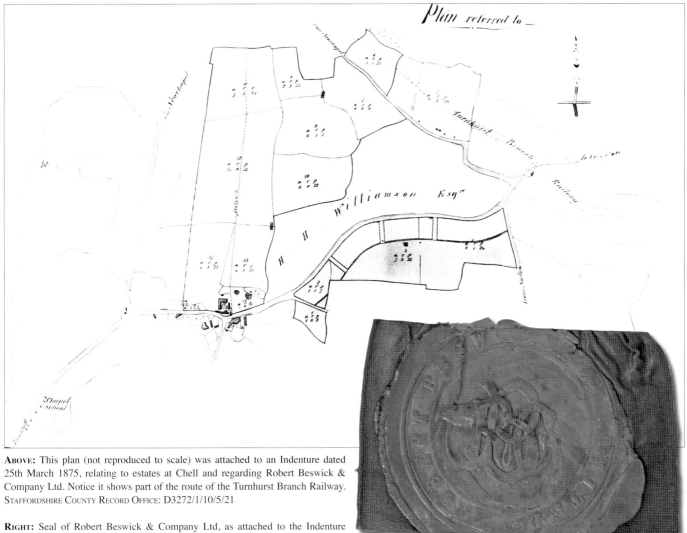

Plan referred to

ABOVE: This plan (not reproduced to scale) was attached to an Indenture dated 25th March 1875, relating to estates at Chell and regarding Robert Beswick & Company Ltd. Notice it shows part of the route of the Turnhurst Branch Railway. STAFFORDSHIRE COUNTY RECORD OFFICE: D3272/1/10/5/21

RIGHT: Seal of Robert Beswick & Company Ltd, as attached to the Indenture referred to above. STAFFORDSHIRE COUNTY RECORD OFFICE: D3272/1/10/5/21

acquired all the leasehold estate rights title and interest in or to the coal cannel ironstone and other mines and minerals so demised and known as Chell Collieries.' The agreement also included *'the right title and interest of the Vendor* [Beswick] *in and over a branch railway and siding known as the Turnhurst Branch Railway and Siding which connects the Turnhurst Estate with the North Staffordshire Railway and runs in its course through a portion of the Chell Estate and which said right title and interest was granted by an Indenture dated the 13 July 1867 and made between Thomas Francis Hazlehurst and the Vendor* [Beswick]*'.* From this we can perhaps deduce that Beswick negotiated an agreement with Hazlehurst to use the railway the latter was building to serve the Turnhurst Estate, as well as the Chell collieries. As the line passed near to the Chell Collieries, a connecting siding or sidings would be quite easy to construct. There is also a reference to an earlier award in favour of Beswick by an independent civil engineer, dated 11th August 1873, following some sort of disagreement over the use of the *'Turnhurst Branch Railway'.* Mention is made in the 1875 agreement with Bishop that the sum in question was £60,000, following a second independent valuation, in this case by a mining engineer on behalf of Bishop.[98] Further mention of this report is made in a later paragraph.

Luke Bishop, with a Queen Anne Street address in London, would appear to have been a financier and in the interregnum between his agreement to purchase the estate and formation of the new company,

various arrangements were made to raise the estimated capital. Some of this was by way of a mortgage and the rest by an allocation of fully paid shares in the new company. Bishop, for example, was allocated 2,270, Beswick 1,500 and his son, Robert Beswick Junior, 100. Beswick Junior was described in the share register as a colliery manager, presumably of the Chell Collieries. Other significant shareholders were Archibald Douglas of Gloucester Terrace in Hyde Park, described as a civil engineer with 100 shares, William Marshall, a brewer and maltster of Bayswater, also with 100 shares and Robert Carr, an engineering surveyor, once again London based, with 395 shares. Subsequently, 650 shares were issued to John Smith Betts, an accountant from Eastcote in Middlesex, following an agreement dated 13th February 1875. Like Bishop, Betts was involved in financing the purchase. The first directors of the new company were Luke Bishop, Robert Beswick Junior, Robert Carr and Archibald Douglas, with John Betts the Secretary.

A report by Archibald Douglas, once again described as a civil engineer and dated 11th August 1874, refers to Chell Colliery being served by a private standard gauge railway, one and a quarter miles long. The report mentions that the line was laid with 70lbs per yard rail, that there was one locomotive engine, forty-five standard gauge wagons variously of 8- and 10-ton capacity, and an engine shed. A narrow gauge railway consisted of 4,000 yards of 28lbs per yard tram rail and there were forty-five tram wagons. This is the report mentioned above in connection with the formation of Robert Beswick & Company Ltd.

As with the Chell Coal & Iron Company Ltd, this company does not appear to have been in business very long. As early as 5th June 1877, the NSR directors minutes record the fact that Beswick & Company [sic] had gone into liquidation owing the company £260.[99] On 30th May 1877, the Manchester & Liverpool & District Banking Company, of Spring Gardens in Manchester, petitioned the Chancery Division of the High Court of Justice for a winding up order. The bank was a creditor of the company and its petition, supported by Luke Bishop, Archibald Douglas and a number of other creditors, was heard on 30th June 1877. Of the other directors, Betts, Marshall and Carr opposed the petition. After hearing the petitions, the court ordered that the company be wound up and the creditors be paid out of its assets. At an Extraordinary General Meeting on 15th June 1877, it was resolved *'that by reason of its liabilities'* the company to be compulsorily wound up, with Bertram Smart,[100] of Cheapside in London, appointed liquidator. Having said that, it was not until a further Chancery Court hearing on 3rd December 1884, when the final transactions were agreed, that the company was formally dissolved. Unfortunately, such records as exist are silent on what did or did not happen between the dates of the two Chancery Court hearings. On the face of it this would appear to have been yet another company put in place in an effort to raise capital to develop the mining operations. However, quite why two such companies should have been in existence contemporaneously has not only gone unrecorded but stretches the imagination as to what the motives of their respective promoters might have been.[101]

Whatever the ups and downs of these various companies, it would seem that Robert Beswick, along with two of his sons, continued to operate Chell Colliery, sometimes trading as Beswick Brothers. On 20th November 1883, there was a fatal accident at what was described as the Chell Colliery of Beswick Brothers. A 14 year old boy named William Pratt, said to be a 'Taker Off', was trapped at the bottom of a jig by a loaded tub and his injuries proved fatal. The poor lad's job would have been coupling and uncoupling the tramway tubs, the jig being an inclined tramway with self-acting rope haulage.[102] In February 1887,

Robert Beswick senior was declared bankrupt, due, it was said, to debts incurred in unprofitable working of the colliery. However, it would appear from surviving documents that, despite the fact that Beswick senior was the lessee of the mineral rights from Hazlehurst, it was in fact his two sons, Robert junior (1840-1913) and James Wright (1845-1920), who were running the operations and making the managerial decisions. At that time, Robert senior, who would have been in his eighties, was living at Radway Green, just over the border in Cheshire, having delegated day to day management of his interests to his sons; he died in mid 1890. The brothers seem to have also overreached themselves, incurring large debts in rents and Royalties along with various other creditors, including wagon hire and defaults in interest payments to their bankers. Resulting from this, an arrangement was entered into between S. Herbert Cooper, a solicitor acting on behalf of Hazlehurst and the trustees in the bankruptcy of Robert Beswick. The mining leases were surrendered, along with title to the surface property, plant and equipment, to Thomas Francis Hazlehurst, as the lessor of the mineral estate. Hazlehurst had previously made an agreement with the Beswicks in an attempt to lessen their financial burden. It had been agreed that if the lower coal measures could be developed, the pit should become profitable; in the event to no avail. After the bankruptcy of the Beswicks, Hazlehurst worked the colliery under his own auspices but with Robert Beswick as the certified manager along with, one assumes, his brother. However, this was not the end of the matter as, in 1889 and 1890, there were further proceedings in the Court of Chancery. This was a long and complicated affair; suffice it to say that Beswick senior's creditors, via the trustees of his bankruptcy, tried to argue that the agreement reached with Hazlehurst gave the latter a disproportionate share of the Beswick assets, such that they were deprived of what was considered their legitimate share. This was described in court as a fraud of creditors. Despite the claims, after some seven days of hearing evidence, on 15th May 1890, judgement was given in favour of Hazlehurst. Nothing daunted, the trustees appealed against the judgement and the case went to the High Court of Justice which, on 13th November 1890 and after several days hearing all the evidence, dismissed the appeal.

It may be as a result of the bankruptcy of Robert Beswick that a further new company was registered on 18th March 1887, the Chell Colliery Company Ltd. In this case, it was done to adopt an agreement dated 10th February 1887, made between

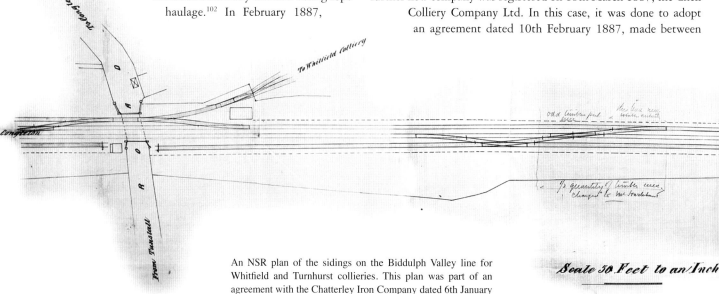

An NSR plan of the sidings on the Biddulph Valley line for Whitfield and Turnhurst collieries. This plan was part of an agreement with the Chatterley Iron Company dated 6th January 1884. NATIONAL ARCHIVES: RAIL 532/175

The first two pages of the Memorandum of Association of the Chell Colliery Company Ltd, which was registered on 18th March 1887 with capital of £60,000. National Archives: BT31/3836/24130)

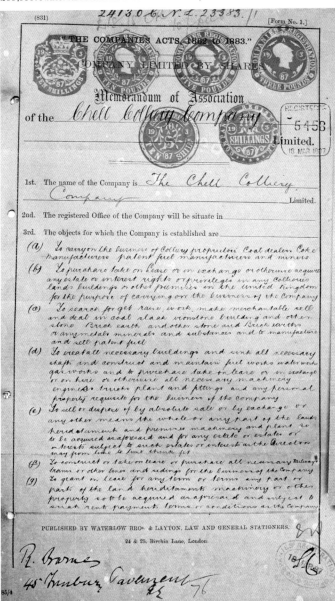

Thomas James Hazlehurst[103] of one part and Charles William Langford as trustee of the company the other part. Unfortunately, the agreement referred to does not appear to have survived. The capital was £60,000 divided in to 60,000 shares of £1 each, with the registered office presumably in London, although this is not mentioned; London was the location of all the subscribers. Like its predecessors, what if anything this company achieved appears to have gone unrecorded, as apart from a return dated 19th April 1887, which tells us little, no others were ever submitted. In November 1891, the Registrar of Joint Stock Companies wrote to R. Barnes, a solicitor of 45 Finsbury Pavement in London, enquiring as to the position of the company as no returns had been submitted. Despite a Richard Barnes of this same address being one of the original subscribers to the company, Barnes replied on 10th November stating, '*I have no knowledge of its position* [the company], *no more I have recollections of having been concerned with it.*' On 16th August 1892, the company was struck off the Register. So once again we are left wondering but two of the subscribers, Henry De Jersey and Edward O. Preston,

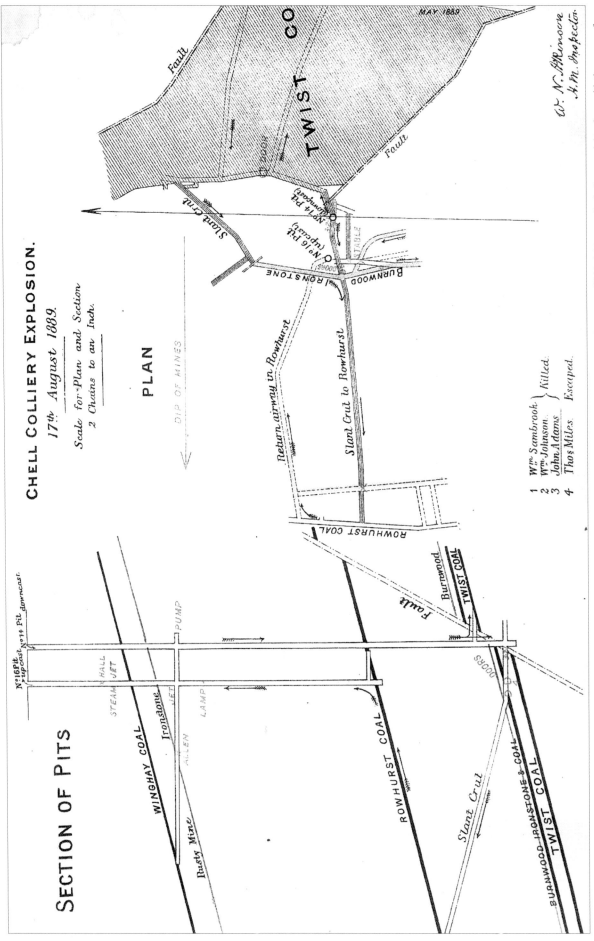

The plan that accompanied Her Majesty's Inspector of Mines' report into the Chell Colliery explosion on 17th August 1889. Notice his signature – W N. Atkinson – in the bottom right, along with the names of the men who lost their lives, centre bottom. Also indicated are the positions of Robert Allen and Frederick Hall when the explosion occurred. This is an interesting plan as it gives us some idea of the extent and layout of the underground workings.

Front page of the annual report for the Tunstall Coal & Iron Company Ltd, for the year ending 31st March 1901. LONDON METROPOLITAN ARCHIVES: GUILD HALL LIBRARY STOCK EXCHANGE ANNUAL COMPANY REPORTS

both of 4 Tokenhouse Buildings, London EC, described themselves as financiers.[104]

On 6th January 1884, Hazlehurst, by this time giving an address of Misterton Hall in Leicestershire, entered into a new siding agreement with the NSR, the railway company making some alterations to the layout. In this case, the annual payments were fixed at just over £61 per annum, payable in four equal instalments and the agreement was to run for fourteen years from December the previous year. In the event, as we shall see, it actually ran until June 1904.[105] By the time of this second agreement, the siding was officially known as Chell Siding. This probably followed quite significant alterations to the siding connections for Chatterley-Whitfield Colliery, necessary when the Biddulph Valley line was converted to double track, as the new set of rails were laid on the east, Chatterley-Whitfield side. The new arrangements for Chatterley-Whitfield were now further south, which enabled the two sets of sidings, Turnhurst Branch (Hazlehurst) and Chatterley-Whitfield, to be worked from one signal box. As mentioned earlier, previously the junction for the Chatterley-Whitfield Colliery sidings was close to the connection with the private line to the Wedgwood and Lane End pits, such that one signal box was able to operate all the connections. However, closure of the line to the Wedgwood and Lane Ends pits, along with conversion of the Biddulph Valley line to double track, presented the opportunity to remodel the arrangements. Both colliery concerns would have been happy with this as it saved them having to fund separately the wages of signalmen and other ancillary costs. An interesting traffic working is referred to in the NSR Weekly Notice for the period 4th to 10th September 1882. Ironstone traffic from Chell Sidings was to be worked to Milton Junction in time to go forward by the 12.55pm train from Froghall to Etruria. The Froghall train would be taking limestone to the Shelton Iron & Steel Works at Etruria where, presumably, the ironstone would also be destined.[106]

At seven thirty in the evening of 17th August 1889, there was a firedamp (gas) explosion at Chell Colliery, due to an accumulation of gas in some old working in the North Twist coal at a depth of 265 yards. It resulted in the deaths of three '*subordinate officers of the colliery*' and the certified manager, Robert Beswick Junior, was charged in connection with the Mine Regulations Act on three counts. In the first for not providing adequate ventilation, in the second for allowing a lamp, or light, not part of a protected safety lamp to be used and, in the third, for allowing the use of unprotected Davy lamps. According to the report of Her Majesty's Inspector of Mines, William N. Atkinson, a large accumulation of gas had been discovered towards the end of July while the manager was inspecting the workings with a view to reopening them. Efforts were made, commencing on 13th August, to disperse the gas by forming a series of stoppings in the workings near the foot of the No. 14 downcast shaft, to allow fresh air to circulate better. As this was only partially successful, on Saturday 17th at one o' clock, when the men had left the pit for the weekend, Beswick instructed seven officials to remain in a determined effort to

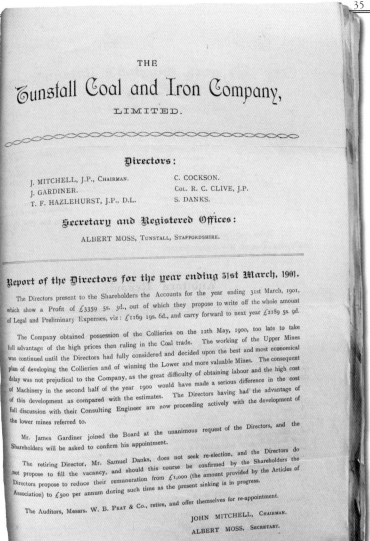

move the gas. The individuals were William Sambrook, the under-manager, accompanied by Frederick Hall, Robert Allen, Thomas Miles (a fireman), Patrick McNally, and Messrs Adams and Johnson (two more firemen). While the pit had been ventilated by a fan at the upcast shaft, this had been discontinued and replaced by steam jets using the exhaust of a Tangye pump engine. More recently, to augment the ventilation, a brazier had been hung in the upcast shaft about 100 yards from the surface. After some time trying to shift the gas gradually, Sambrook resorted to the full force of the ventilating air and it would appear he moved, or had moved, all or part of one of the stoppings. While this was taking place, some of the men were in the No. 16 upcast shaft with unprotected lamps and the rapid movement of the gas, ignited by the unprotected lamps, caused an explosion back towards the bottom of the downcast shaft, resulting in the deaths of Sambrook, Adams and Johnson. The Coroner recorded a verdict of accidental death, adding a rider that great blame was due to the manager. Beswick was fined a total of £30 12s for breaches of the Mines Regulation Act. Even by the standards of the day, this seems a miserable figure for the lives of three men. The Stipendiary Magistrate, however, considered there were extenuating circumstances, in that Beswick had left very clear instructions that the gas was to be moved gradually and that the stoppings were adequate and should not be moved. He considered that Sambrook

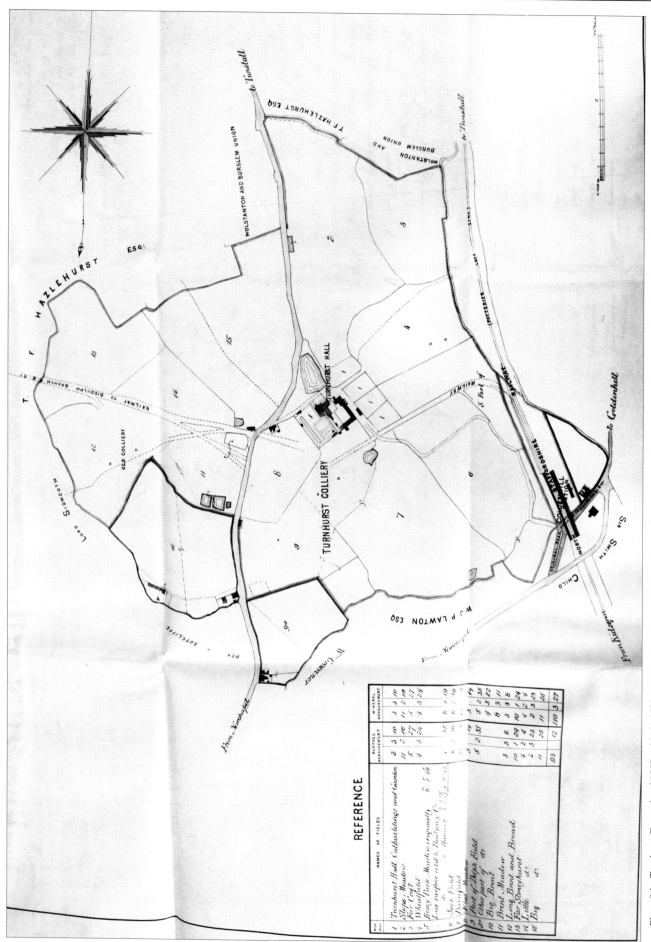

Plan of the Turnhurst Estate dated 1887, with the NSR Potteries Loop Line at Goldenhill to the bottom, along with the course of the private railway from Goldenhill to Turnhurst. To the top can be seen the course of the Turnhurst Branch Railway, which connected with the NSR Biddulph Valley line. The map is part of an Indenture dated 21st January 1887, between Martha Napier and Mary Walker, with Charles James Homer. STAFFORDSHIRE COUNTY RECORD OFFICE: D3272/1/10/5/17

was partly responsible for the explosion in disregarding Beswick's instructions to move the gas gradually and that at least one stopping had been moved, if not under Sambrook's instructions, then by person or persons unknown.[107]

As mentioned earlier, on 3rd April 1900, yet another limited liability company was registered, the Tunstall Coal & Iron Company Ltd, to acquire the Chell and Turnhurst collieries from T.F. Hazlehurst and James Gardiner, trading as the Chell Colliery Company. The purchase price was £50,000, with Gardiner, of New Broad Street in London, a joint promoter with Hazlehurst. Gardiner appears to have been enlisted to assist in the process of floatation, as there is no evidence that he was ever actively involved with the physical operations. Hazlehurst, incidentally, gave his earlier address of Cold Ashby Hall, Rugby. A prospectus was duly issued, offering for public subscription 75,000 £1 shares from an authorised capital of £100,000. The residual authorised capital was not planned to be issued at the outset but held back, as it equated to the estimated capital investment required to increase the output at Chell from between 40,000 and 50,000 to 150,000 tons per annum. The list of directors was impressive. As well as Hazlehurst, they comprised Samuel Danks of Hadley Park in Wellington, a well respected engineer and boilermaker; Colonel Robert C. Clive JP, managing director of the nearby Clanway Colliery of Clive, Son & Myott Ltd; John Mitchell JP, who was the chairman, as well as holding a similar position on the board of the Foxfield Colliery Company Ltd near Cheadle; and Charles Cockson, who had been general manager of the Ince Coal & Cannel Company at Ince Hall Colliery near Wigan. The secretary was Albert Moss. Danks soon resigned and Gardiner was, in fact, his replacement.

The two shafts at Chell were 270 and 200 yards deep, and were known as No's 14 and 16; No. 14 had double head gears, whereas No. 16 was single. They were both served by a pair of horizontal steam winding engines, with cylinders 25½ins x 48ins and 10ft diameter drums. There was an emergency engine also attached to the No. 14 shaft, with a single cylinder 9ins x 14ins. In addition, there was another pair of horizontal engines with cylinders 24ins x 60ins that had not been installed and were 'intended for sinking'. This would have been either for new shafts or deepening the existing ones; more likely the latter. There were other engines for ventilation, pumping and driving machinery, including one underground at the No. 14 shaft, steam being supplied by three Lancashire boilers. Screening of the coal was provided by a patent coal screen by Rigg, arranged for loading coal into railway wagons, with a further coal screen at Chell that had accommodation for loading carts, six at a time. Turnhurst Colliery, which may not have been drawing coal at the time, consisted of two 10ft diameter shafts

250 yards deep. However, developments had been under way and a pair of horizontal winding engines with 26ins x 54ins cylinders had recently been erected, although it would appear that this engine had not been commissioned. This helps confirm that Turnhurst Colliery had been 'standing', to use a local term and that it was the intention of the company to commence working it again with at least some new equipment.

Of particular interest are the items of railway equipment. According to an inventory of assets (see Appendix II) compiled as part of the agreement to form the limited company, they owned seventy main line wagons, consisting of twenty 8-tonners and fifty of 10-ton capacity. There is mention of a railway of about 900 yards connecting the colliery with the Biddulph Valley Branch of the NSR, along with 'a railway from the Turnhurst Branch to Chell with sidings on the colliery of about 1,750 yards. Ninety six yards of rails forming a cart road from Chell screens to the highway. All necessary pit waggons, rails and sleepers, jigs, ropes, chains underground.' It would seem, therefore, from this description and early maps, that a railway of some sort existed from the screens at Chell Colliery to a landsale wharf at the village of Chell, adjacent to the Biddulph road (the present day A527). However, reference to this being a cart road and mention of the screens at Chell being capable of loading carts might lead one to believe that this was not a railway in the accepted sense.[108]

An interesting aspect regarding the Turnhurst Branch is the reference to the 900 yards of railway connecting the colliery with the NSR. This would suggest that the line was only in place as far as Chell Colliery and not onwards to Turnhurst. This is confirmed by the estate plan accompanying the mineral lease agreement, which marks the course of the line at the Turnhurst end as 'Old Railway to Biddulph Branch NSR'. Likewise, the 1898 6 inch OS map shows the line as removed beyond where the connection branched off to the Chell and Oxford pits. However, the narrow gauge rope-hauled line from Turnhurst to Goldenhill is shown on both the estate plan and the 1898 OS map as still in situ. Whether or not the standard gauge line to Turnhurst was ever reinstated in the short life of the new operator is a matter of conjecture but on the balance of the evidence it would seem unlikely.

Even more interestingly, in the inventory is mention of a locomotive: 'Clara, saddle tank, inside cylinders ten and a half inch diameter 20 inch stroke, six wheels coupled 3 feet 3 inch diameter, copper firebox and stays, brass tubes etc., comparatively new.' Prior to the

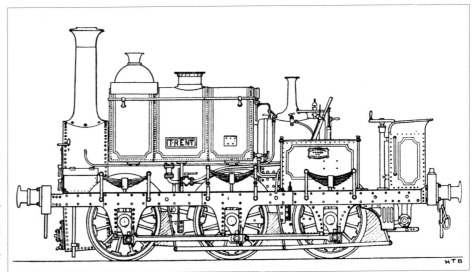

This drawing shows the Chell locomotive *Trent*, formerly a Manchester & Birmingham Railway engine built in 1842. It was rebuilt by Issac Watt Boulton at his famous siding at Ashton-under-Lyne into the form shown here. TAKEN FROM *THE CHRONICLES OF BOULTON'S SIDING*

This photograph was taken on 26th June 1952, looking north from the bridge that took the Whitfield-Pinnox Mineral Railway over the Biddulph Valley line. In the centre distance the remains of the embankment of the Turnhurst Branch Railway can be seen curving away to the left, behind the signal post. By this time, as can be seen, the embankment had been partly breached. The buildings to the right are part of Chatterley-Whitfield Colliery and on the skyline is the dirt tip of Victoria Colliery at Black Bull, formerly owned by Robert Heath & Sons. Dr JACK HOLLICK

Taken just over a year later, on 16th August 1953, this view is looking south from just beyond the former junction with the Turnhurst Branch Railway. Notice the remains of the embankment to the right, which has been cut-back even further, along with the new housing developments at Fegg Hayes. Dr JACK HOLLICK

The 1876-built Head Wrightson vertical boiler locomotive that worked at Chell and Turnhurst collieries, possibly from new. This photograph of the engine was taken circa 1899, when it was in the ownership of contractor Stephen Offer and engaged on construction of the Cheadle Railway, south of Stoke-on-Trent.

discovery of this inventory, three locomotives are recorded as having been used at these pits, none of which fits the description of *Clara*.[109] There is a relevant reference in Alfred Rosling Bennett's classic book *The Chronicles of Boulton's Siding* (Locomotive Publishing Company, 1927) of an old Sharp Roberts & Company locomotive built as long ago as 1842, maker's No. 199. This locomotive had originally been supplied to the Manchester & Birmingham Railway as its No. 12, an 0-4-2 tender engine with inside cylinders 14in x 20ins and 4ft 6ins diameter coupled wheels. After a varied life, Boulton acquired it from the London & North Western Railway towards the end of 1864, at which time it carried No. 1368 and the name *Trent*. Over the next few years, Boulton hired *Trent* to a number of operators and, in May 1871, undertook a quite extensive reconstruction. The engine was converted into a six coupled saddle tank with 4ft diameter wheels and sold shortly after, for the sum of £800, to the Cowbridge Railway in Glamorgan.[110] However, he later bought *Trent* back and, in August 1873, sold the engine, this time at the slightly higher price of £850, to what Bennett refers to in his book as '*the Chell Ironstone Mines*'. It has always been assumed that these mines are one and the same as those we are here discussing. Whatever the case, the trail immediately goes cold and no other information has ever come to light on the engine's fate but it is clearly not one and the same as *Clara*. Nevertheless, *Trent* probably lasted at Chell for around fifteen to twenty years and if kept in good condition, would have been well capable of working the steeply graded Turnhurst Branch Railway.

The second engine was an interesting type of vertical boiler locomotive, albeit a familiar design of its builder, the Thornaby-on-Tees based Head Wrightson & Company. Unlike most manufacturers' designs of vertical boiler locomotives, which have vertical engines driving a cranked axle, sometimes via a gear train, this locomotive had conventional outside cylinders directly coupled to the wheels. It was maker's No. 35 and its year of construction was 1876. We have no knowledge of this engine's early history and it may have been acquired new. Based on photographs, it had cylinders of only about 9ins diameter at the most; whatever its source, it would seem a strange purchase in view of the gradients of the lines where it worked. We do know from photographic evidence that it was later in the ownership of Stephen Offer, who was at that time – 1897-1900 – the contractor for part of the Cheadle Railway. This is the Staffordshire Cheadle, just south of Stoke-on-Trent. Stephen Offer (1852-1930) was a native of Midsomer Norton in Somerset and by around 1878, the under-manager of Robert Heath's Norton Colliery at Ford Green. He later moved to Cheadle, where he was heavily involved, both financially and physically, in mining operations connected with the Cheadle coalfield. A prominent member of the local community, he also took a great interest in various schemes to build a railway to connect the town with the NSR. A partner in some of his mining activities, James Lockett, was also involved with the railway when Offer took on the task of completing its construction, as mentioned above. The two of them were later, towards the end

Plan (not reproduced to scale) of Chatterley-Whitfield Colliery mining boundaries as existing in 1873 and 1924. Although the original of this plan is coloured to indicate the boundaries at the two dates, it is nevertheless felt worthy of inclusion as it does show the relative positions of the various colliery undertakings. The dates when the various mining rights were acquired by the colliery subsequent to 1873 are, however, noted in the small circles. The plan also illustrates the relative position of the main line railways and the private colliery line to Tunstall, along with its connections to the main lines at both the colliery and Tunstall. KEELE UNIVERSITY ARCHIVES: WILLIAM JACK COLLECTION, CHATTERLEY-WHITFIELD COLLIERY DOCUMENTS. (*Note: This plan is contained in an untitled book of miscellaneous documents and notes*)

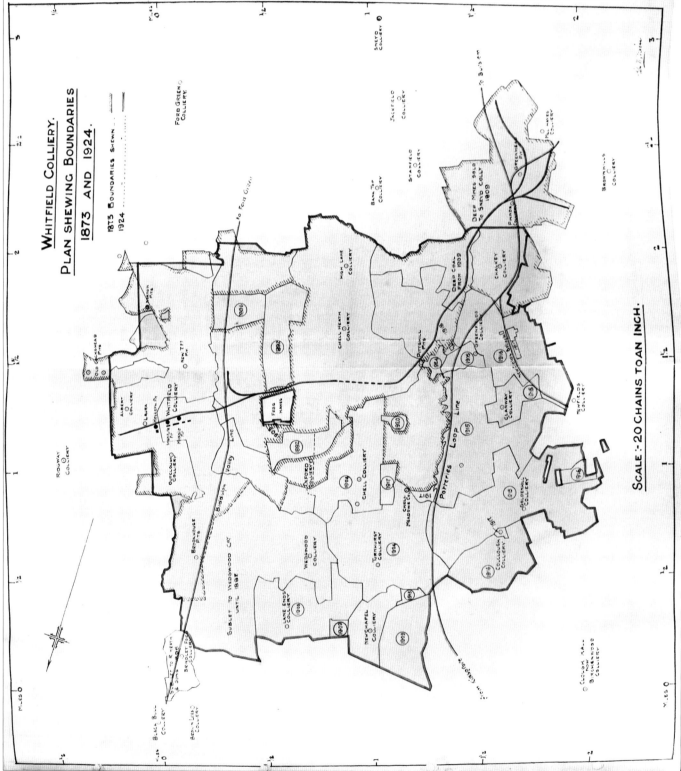

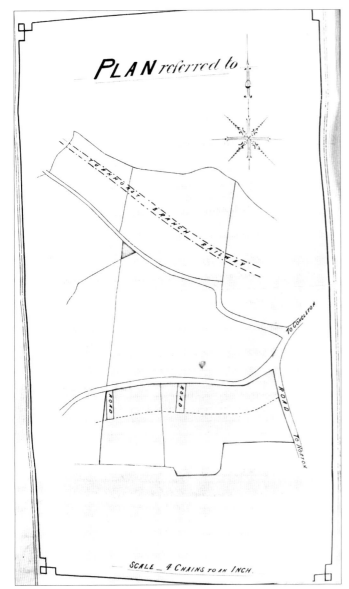

This plan was part of an agreement between T.F. Hazlehurst and Chatterley-Whitfield Collieries Ltd, dated 1st March 1898, regarding mining leases. It is interesting from our point of view as it shows part of the course of the Turnhurst Branch Railway. To enable interested readers to locate the exact position of the map, the junction between the Congleton and Norton roads is at OS SJ 877533. STAFFORDSHIRE COUNTY RECORD OFFICE: D3272/1/10/5/21

of the 19th century, involved in coal mining in the Kidsgrove area. Offer's earlier connections at Norton could well be how he became aware of this vertical boilered locomotive, which would have been ideal for contracting use. It might also have been available at the time he needed motive power to assist with his railway construction works on the Cheadle Railway.[111] Last but by no means least, there was a locomotive called *Nora*, stated to have been a four-coupled saddle tank of which more will be said later.

The new company obtained possession of the colliery on 12th May 1900 and immediately started to work the upper mines, while surveys were undertaken to establish the best way of getting the lower and more valuable coal seams. For the year ending 31st March 1901, a profit of £3,359 was recorded, against which £1,170 was written off as the cost of the legal and preliminary expenses incurred in forming the new company. The share capital of £100,000 was subscribed to the tune of £67,942 but no dividend was declared,

the directors recommending the profit be carried over against continuing development costs. Other interesting figures in the first balance sheet regard the valuation of the assets: mining property – £47,750; machinery and plant – £4,500; railway wagons – £3,125; new development account, which included expenses during the year in connection with new works, machinery and plant and a railway siding – £1,437. It was soon discovered that a considerable portion of the Twist coal seam in the Oxford Estate that the prospectus claimed to be available had, in fact, already been got. The lease of some of the minerals in this part of the estate was subject to an agreement of 1st March 1898, between Hazlehurst and Chatterley-Whitfield Collieries Ltd.[112] The two parties had agreed on a mutual swap of mineral leases, as it was felt by Hazlehurst that the Oxford mines in question could be better got as part of his Chell Colliery. Likewise, Chatterley-Whitfield gained access to coals better extracted via its existing pits. When Counsel's Opinion was commissioned by solicitors on behalf of Hazlehurst, it was pointed out that this 'trespass', as it was termed, had been committed some years earlier when Robert Beswick and his various associates had been working the mines. More damningly, it was also discovered that the trespass had continued in more recent times, when Hazlehurst himself was working the colliery with, be it mentioned, Beswick as his manager. The claim by the new company was that Hazlehurst was responsible for the lack of information in the prospectus and that compensation should be made based on the estimated profit had the missing coal still been there. It would appear that the new company was hoping to extract this coal relatively easily and in doing so help to raise the additional capital to invest in developing the lower coal seams at both Chell and Turnhurst. It was, of course, the ease with which this coal could be got that presumably encouraged Beswick to take it in the first place, although he had no authority to do so. Counsel's brief mentioned that relations between the two men were strained and that Beswick was no longer manager.

In their report for the year ending 31st March 1901, the directors also mentioned the difficulty in obtaining labour and the high cost of machinery. In the following year's report, ending on 31st March again, mention is made of serious difficulties encountered due to a large and unexpected influx of water into the workings, which the existing pumping plant had been unable to handle. However, sinking of the shafts to a deeper level to reach the Birchenwood coal seam had proceeded and it was estimated that, in twenty-one weeks, the sinking would be complete. Despite what had been achieved, it was becoming clear that the company was in serious financial trouble. Expenditure on new machinery and plant amounted to no less than £12,172 and there was a liability of £2,841 on additional railway wagons that had been taken on hire purchase. As it already had a fleet of railway wagons, obviously the company was anticipating a significant increase in production. Sales of coal and ironstone totalled but £2,587, with a profit and loss account debit of £2,432 going forward. This was despite Hazlehurst having to find £1,500 under the agreement with him as part of the purchase arrangements, due to the water problem. An interesting item in the profit and loss account is the sum of £1,622, for coal used '*at boilers and loco*'. Despite the expenditure on new machinery and plant, which included more powerful pumping engines that the directors stated were coping with the water, the shareholders were not happy. Adding to their problems, they were being asked to support a recommendation by the directors for a £20,000 debenture issue bearing interest at

In the High Court of Justice   0083 *of 1904*
Companies Winding Up
Mr Justice Buckley

In the Matter of the Companies Acts 1862 to 1900
                              and
In the Matter of The Tunstall Coal & Iron
Company Limited

*I William Barclay Peat of No 3 Lothbury in
the City of London Chartered Accountant the
Liquidator of the above named Company make oath
and say as follows:—*

1.   *The above named Company The Tunstall Coal
& Iron Company (hereinafter called "the Company")
was incorporated on the 31st day of March 1900 with
a capital of £100000 divided into One hundred thousand
shares of One pound each for the purpose of carrying
on the business of Colliery Proprietors and other the
objects set forth in the Memorandum of Association of
the Company*

2.   *Thomas Francis Hazlehurst of Cold Ashby Hall
in the County of Northampton was one of the promoters
of the Company and under a contract dated the
10th day of October 1899 made between the said Thomas
Francis Hazlehurst of the one part and James Gardiner
(another promoter of the Company) of the other part
agreed to grant to the Company (the formation of
which was then contemplated) the two leases hereinafter
mentioned and to sell to the Company all plant
machinery stock in trade and rolling stock at both
Collieries in consideration of the sum of £25000*

First page of a 1904 High Court of Justice hearing under the provisions of the Companies Act, regarding liquidation of the Tunstall Coal & Iron Company Ltd. NATIONAL ARCHIVES: J13/3837

5½%. To add insult to injury, it was also suggested that the existing shareholders be invited to subscribe! In June 1903, the inevitable result was a decision for voluntary liquidation and although, as we shall see later, there was a scheme proposed by the directors for a financial reconstruction, nothing came of it. The company was finally dissolved on 6th March 1905, of which more anon.[113] Worth a brief mention is that, in accordance with mining legislation, the underground plans for those parts of the underground workings which were not subject to the lease arrangements with Hazlehurst and were not worked, were deposited with the Home Department on 22nd May 1902.

We have some knowledge why this latest and, as events turned out, last attempt to directly mine the Chell and Turnhurst minerals was unsuccessful. It would seem that the original intention was not only to develop the extraction of minerals from newly developed seams; it was also to work others that had been available from the Oxford Colliery but had not in fact been touched. In the view of the promoters of the new company, much profitable coal remained to be had. Current output of Chell Colliery was, as quoted earlier, between 40,000 and 50,000 tons per annum. James Lucas, a mining engineer and formerly managing director of the Shelton Iron, Steel & Coal Company Ltd, in a report commissioned for, inter alia, the share issue, opined that with a capital expenditure of around £20,000 to £25,000, this could be increased to 150,000 tons of coal and 50,000 tons of calcined ironstone per annum. As well as this report by Lucas, the promoters commissioned a second one by a Lancashire-based civil and mining engineer, J.H. Lake. Both Lake and Lucas valued the undertaking at around £60,000. Robert Beswick junior, as the manager of Chell Collieries, reckoned that an annual profit of £15,000 was a moderate estimate. Lake was doubtless a nominee of fellow Lancastrian and director Charles Cookson. Although at this distance in time we have no detailed knowledge as to the exact remit of Lucas and Lake, two apparently eminent mining engineers, insofar as the underground works were concerned they do not seem to have done those investing in the new company any favours, including Hazlehurst. In particular, they do not appear to have gone underground, or if they did, their examination was somewhat less extensive that might have been expected.

As early as November 1902, James Gardiner had approached Chatterley-Whitfield Collieries to sound out its interest, if any, in the Chell and Turnhurst undertaking. Shrewdly, the officials of the colliery company played down any great enthusiasm, although, as will become evident, they were interested in the mining rights but not the shafts and surface equipment. In July 1903, Robert Heath & Sons Ltd started to take an interest in the mines and this prompted Chatterley-Whitfield to write to Hazlehurst, as the owner of the mineral rights, offering to meet and discuss the issue. This was a difficult time for Hazlehurst, as although he was the owner of the mineral rights of the Chell and Turnhurst estates, he was also a director of the Tunstall company which had just gone into liquidation. Chatterley-Whitfield was of the view that much of the Cockshead coal on the top side of the High Lane fault could be worked by extension of its existing underground operations, as otherwise the Turnhurst shafts would have to be driven to a depth of at least half a mile to reach the same seams. At that time, Chatterley-Whitfield had just acquired the mineral rights of the Lane Ends Estate, which adjoined those of Turnhurst. While expressing his interest, Hazlehurst mentioned that although the Tunstall company was in liquidation, it was still in existence and as the mineral rights were still on lease to that company, he could do nothing without the approval of the liquidator. He suggested an offer be made to the liquidator to lease the whole Tunstall undertaking, on the basis that when the mines came back into his hands, a lease of the mineral rights could continue. Chatterley-Whitfield, however, had no interest in the surface plant, as it intended, as mentioned above, to get the coal via its existing underground workings. In October 1903, the liquidator, William Barclay Peat, made it known that he was going to advertise the complete undertaking for sale by private treaty and, if not sold, Hazlehurst would be obliged under his agreements when the company was formed to purchase the surface and underground plant at a valuation. Hazlehurst then suggested to Chatterley-Whitfield that, in such an event, if the colliery company would take the plant, etc. off his hands at the same price he paid, he would then lease the minerals of the Turnhurst and Chell estates to the colliery company. He proposed a minimum rent of £1,000 per annum and the same extraction rates the colliery company was already paying for other mines it held on lease from him. As events transpired, the liquidator

Although not a locomotive that worked at Chell or Turnhurst, *Roger* of Chatterley-Whitfield Colliery is nevertheless mentioned in the text. It came to Whitfield from Hucknall Colliery in Nottinghamshire, via Longbottom, a Wakefield dealer and was later sold for scrap along with the former Chell locomotive *Norah*.

was unable to sell the whole undertaking, leaving the issue of the surface plant and equipment one that Hazlehurst had to manage.

The issue rumbled on into the following year, with Hazlehurst anxious not to have to buy the surface and underground plant and equipment but equally anxious to lease his mineral rights. The liquidator, meanwhile, was similarly anxious to get as much money as he could from the plant and equipment, to enable him to clear the outstanding creditors and, if possible, give a return to the shareholders. At the same time, in trying to persuade Chatterley-Whitfield to help him out regarding the plant and equipment and while willing to agree very favourable terms for the mineral rights, Hazlehurst was anxious not to let the liquidator know of the colliery company's interest. His reasoning was that if the liquidator knew that an existing colliery company was interested, any views he might have on their value would increase! The existing mineral lease, incidentally, was for forty-two years from 1901, with options to renew. An interesting statistic that appears in the Chatterley-Whitfield Officials minute books, from which much of this particular part of the narrative stems, was that the Tunstall company paid an annual rent to the NSR of £60 for siding rent, with a notice period on both sides of three months. It then transpired that the liquidator also wanted some consideration from whoever purchased the surface plant and equipment, for the investment made by the Tunstall company in improving and deepening the shafts. Hazlehurst repudiated this very strongly, on the basis that his lease with the Tunstall company only provided for such a consideration if a purchaser required the plant and equipment with a view to using the shafts. Even then, the valuation had to be on the basis of removing

the plant and equipment as opposed to its use as part of an on-going operation. To cut a long story short, the liquidator wanted £6,000 for the surface property, plant and equipment, which would allow him to settle all the creditors, including £625 owing for railway wagon hire[114] and pay the shareholders one shilling in the pound – not a very good return for them it has to be added. In December 1903, Chatterley-Whitfield agreed to pay £3,500 so as to settle the matter. This was later increased under pressure to £3,750, as Hazlehurst felt that the lowest price the liquidator might accept was £4,000. Remember, he was acting as the intermediary between the two parties with one not knowing who the other was!

We now move to the High Court of Justice, 'Companies Winding Up' on 12th April 1904, the case being heard by Mr Justice Buckley. The hearing was largely concerned with an affidavit of William Barclay Peat, chartered accountant and liquidator of the Tunstall Coal & Iron Company Ltd. In his statement, Peat mentions that the purchase price paid by the company to Hazlehurst for the leases of the Turnhurst, Chell and part of the Oxford mineral estates, along with the surface equipment, was £25,000 in cash and the residual in shares in the new concern. The various leases were dated 14th and 25th June 1900. It was shortly after the new company started to work the upper measures of coal that the trespass was discovered, as outlined in Chapter VI, along with a large influx of water, the latter considered to be in consequence of the trespass. This led to a claim by the company against Hazlehurst and two agreements mentioned earlier were made between the parties. To reiterate and help readers understanding at this point, the first, dated 12th April 1901 and for the sum of £1,250, was compensation for the coal that had already

Another locomotive not directly connected with Chell and Turnhurst, the second *Roger* was photographed at Pinnox Sidings, Tunstall on 21st March 1958. Like the earlier *Roger*, it is also mentioned in the text. In the case of the locomotive seen here, it remained in use at the colliery until 1964 and was scrapped the following year. For many years it was the regular shunting engine at Pinnox Sidings, travelling to and from the colliery via the Whitfield-Pinnox Mineral Railway each day. Jim Peden collection, Industrial Railway Society

been mined, while the second, dated 11th June 1901 and for £1,500, was a sum considered sufficient to purchase and install pumping equipment adequate to control the level of water. These agreements, despite Hazlehurst's apparent culpability, appear to have been weighted in his favour, as the money was not payable in cash, rather to be deducted from rents and Royalties due to him under the lease agreements and only then after the minimum rents had been paid. When the company went into liquidation, it had been unable, despite the investment, to control the influx of water. Although Hazlehurst had been paid under the above agreements a few pence short of £731, he was still in credit to the tune of £2,019. While it had been the intention of the directors and a number of shareholders to reconstruct the company with, hopefully, an injection of new capital, there were in the event far to many dissenting shareholders, such that this did not take place. The total number of shares issued and credited as fully paid was 68,250, of which Hazlehurst held 19,278.

Peat was obviously having considerable problems in sorting out this mess, hence his recourse to the court. The assets of the company consisted of very little, as once again Hazlehurst seems to have negotiated himself into a very favourable position when the company was formed. The mineral leases were forfeitable in the event of the company going into liquidation and were therefore worthless as assets. In addition, there was a sum of £650 outstanding as minimum rent, that Hazlehurst would be able to claim against the assets of the company. To cut the rest of this sorry tale somewhat short, Peat had already paid Hazlehurst almost £1,036, a figure which included

the £650 for rents and Royalties, while the company's banks held debentures to the tune of £2,000. Peat had provisionally agreed, following what he claimed to be '*long negotiations*', that subject to the agreement of the court, the sale of the assets of the company back to Hazlehurst could be concluded for the sum of £5,500. Hazlehurst would then relinquish all or any claims he had, or may have, against the company. This would give Peat sufficient funds to pay all the creditors but it left precious little for the disgruntled shareholders – Peat described this as '*a small return*'. On 11th May 1904, the court issued its ruling which was in agreement with Peat's recommendation. Worth mentioning is a statement by Peat that railway wagons on lease to the company had been taken back by the owners and their claim for breach of contract was another of the creditors he had to satisfy.[115]

After Peat's recourse to the Court of Chancery, agreement was eventually reached at £5,500, with Chatterley-Whitfield claiming back from Hazlehurst £1,500, to be deducted from future Royalties due to him on coal subsequently got. The new lease term of thirty-one years was agreed on 21st March 1904, at £100 per yard thick per acre for coal and 9d per ton of calcined ironstone; any coal used for the winding and pumping engine boilers was to be Royalty free.[116] On 3rd June 1904, at a meeting at Chell House, the liquidator gave formal possession of the colliery to Hazlehurst, with John Mitchell representing the Tunstall company.[117] Plans of the workings of the Twist, Winghay, Rowhurst and Burnwood coal were handed over, along with those covering the New Mine ironstone.

Chatterley-Whitfield Collieries Ltd, having got what it wanted, the lease of the mineral rights, was left with the surface plant and equipment which it did not want. Initially it engaged a local engineer and boiler maker, Leveson Wedgwood of Cobridge, to make an independent valuation. Unfortunately, we do not have the figure he established but we do know that, while he pointed out that several items from the inventory provided by Hazlehurst were missing, there were in his words, *'hundreds of pounds of additional material'*. Adverts were placed in various trade journals and the Sheffield-based scrap dealer and machinery dealer Thomas W. Ward Ltd was invited to make an offer. In September 1904, Ward offered £900, which included all the costs associated with removal. Not surprisingly, this was considered far too low. In the event, the equipment appears to have been either sold piecemeal, or moved to Chatterley-Whitfield Colliery. However, some offers were turned down. For example, when in October 1904 a boilermaker from Goldenhill called Ebrill expressed an interest in one of the Tinker's-built Lancashire boilers, he was quoted £300 for one or £570 if he would take the two that existed. He appears to have turned this down as, in January 1906, the two boilers, 30ft long and 8ft in diameter and with a working pressure of 120lbs, were moved to Whitfield Colliery when they were valued at £325 each. The largest of the pit headgears went to Hills' Plymouth Company for £100, loaded on rail in January 1905, while the local Berry Hill Colliery, in February the following year, acquired some hauling and 'tackle' engines, the latter with cylinders 12ins x 24ins, at a total cost of £210. In October 1906, Astley & Tydesley Colliery in Lancashire bought some pumping equipment and associated engines, along with some other 'tackle'. As we will see later, the locomotive *Norah*, like the boilers, was moved to Whitfield. On 20th March 1906, in discussions regarding removal of some ironstone refuse dumped on the surface, Hazlehurst mentioned that the rail connection with the NSR was to be severed shortly. Despite this, no agreement was reached on a price and we are left to conclude that the refuse remained on site.

It is perhaps worth mentioning that, despite the earlier issues between Thomas Hazlehurst and the Beswicks, they continued to be jointly involved in mining operations at both Chell and Turnhurst. Until that is, this final split. By this time, Robert Beswick senior would have passed away, although son Robert and James Wright remained involved to the bitter end.

Reverting to the locomotives, the late Harry Averill, who latterly had charge of the wagon shop at Whitfield, in a letter to Bill Jack said: *'Loco ex-Chell Colliery, which closed in 1902, an 0-4-0 with elongated boiler, about 10 years old at the time, only steamed once after arrival, too small, unsuccessful in attempts to sell and scrapped. Named* Nora *or* Norah.*'* Harry lived at Chell and recalled to Bill riding on the locomotive when a young boy; he was born in 1892. Now I am inclined to think that *Clara* and *Norah* could be one and the same, despite one being described as 4-wheeled and the other 6-wheeled. Although the names are spelt quite differently, phonetically they are similar and it is quite possible whoever compiled the inventory got it wrong. Likewise, Harry might have been confused over the wheel arrangement. Whatever the case, we are none the wiser as regards the engine's identity but Harry's comment that it was *'about 10 years old'* when it came to Whitfield and the inventory record of 1901 stating it was *'comparatively new'* would help in substantiating that the two locomotives were in fact one and the same. The Chatterley-Whitfield officials minute books record at an 11th January 1905 meeting: *'locomotive* Norah, *ex-Chell, if worked will probably require a new firebox.'* At a 6th February 1905 meeting, in discussions regarding a second hand locomotive being offered by Thomas W. Ward,[118] mention was made that Ward was offering £100 each for the locomotives *Roger*[119] and the *'old Chell loco'*; this must be a reference to *Norah*. The minutes further record, on 17th February 1905, that *Gidlow* had been purchased for £525 delivered to Chell Sidings and that *Roger* and *Nora* (spelt thus on this occasion) were to go in part exchange. *Gidlow* appears to have arrived by rail but a minute of 14th April 1905 mentions that, in view of its condition, the NSR would not allow *Roger* to travel by rail, so it was *'broken up at home'* but whether or not by Ward's men, is not recorded. The dealer's offer for this locomotive, by the way, had been reduced to £75. While there is no further mention in the minutes regarding *Norah*, I think it is a fair bet it met the same fate.[120]

The first of four photographs illustrating the remains of the Turnhurst Branch Railway in about 1970. This first view is from close to the site of the colliery at Turnhurst. JOHN HANCOCK.

Working progressively down the route of the Turnhurst Branch Railway in about 1970, towards the junction with the Biddulph Valley line. Prominent in the background of all of the photographs is the chimney and spoil tip of Chatterley-Whitfield Colliery. ALL JOHN HANCOCK

VII
ROBERT HEATH & SONS LTD: OPERATIONS AT NEWCHAPEL AND TURNHURST

In May 1906, John H. Cole, the mining engineer of Robert Heath & Sons Ltd, approached the Chatterley-Whitfield Colliery officials committee, to enquire if his company could sub-lease the Burnwood ironstone on the Turnhurst Estate of Thomas Hazlehurst. He also requested powers to open up the pits at Turnhurst and work the ironstone in conjunction with its existing underground workings. We saw in the previous chapter how Chatterley-Whitfield came to take on the master lease of these mines from Thomas Hazlehurst, after the demise of the Tunstall Coal & Iron Company Ltd. The officials suggested that a formal application be made, with a detailed list of exactly what was being suggested, which resulted in lengthy correspondence and a number of meetings over the next year or so. The colliery company was variously represented by general manager Edward Brownfield Wain, Robert Winstanley, the mining engineer, and John Chear, the secretary. For Heaths it was Cole, who on one occasion, when the issues were getting near completion, was accompanied by Robert Heath (the 2nd 1851-1932) in person. Hazlehurst was present on some occasions too, along with his mining engineer Richard Steele. Heaths wanted to work the mines from the fault running through the Lane Ends Estate, north of the large fault on the south side between Turnhurst

and Chell. They also wanted surface rights, including the use of the shafts at Turnhurst. There was some haggling over sub-leasing and payments required by Chatterley-Whitfield, Hazlehurst's Royalties and the colliery company wanting to retain the right to mine the lower coal seams underneath where Heaths wanted the ironstone. A difficult issue at one point was Hazlehurst wanting Heaths to mine, and therefore pay Royalties, on all the coal in the area it was proposed to sub-lease, down to and including the Twist coal. This was on the basis that if Heaths did not mine this coal, nobody would and any Royalties would be lost to him. Likewise, he wanted them to take to take the Brown Mine ironstone. Heaths were adamant that while they would take the coal, it would only be if it was a profitable exercise for them. However, they were not interested in the Brown Mine ironstone as it had been found to be useless, in Cole's words, in their blast furnaces. These were quite reasonable requirements one would think. Hazlehurst was also concerned about a Heath proposal to remove the barrier to the north, as they wanted to work the mines in conjunction with existing operations at Newchapel. Concerns were expressed by both Chatterley-Whitfield and Hazlehurst about Heaths using any of the existing railway lines serving the pits and connected with the NSR, although it is not clear why. In the event,

Page from a Royalty payment book of Robert Heath & Sons for Newchapel Colliery, covering the period September 1873 to March 1874. This is a good illustration of the sort of documentation and detail that would have been recorded in those times. STAFFORDSHIRE COUNTY RECORD OFFICE: D5420/8

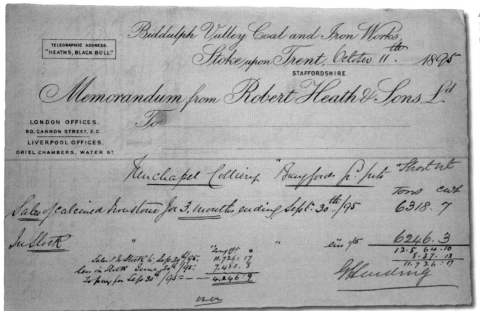

A memorandum from Robert Heath & Sons' Biddulph Valley Coal & Iron Works, relating to Royalty payments due on minerals extracted from Bayford's pits, dated 11th October 1895. Notice it includes both minerals sold as well as any held on stock. The signature is that of George Harding, Heaths' general manager at that time. Several members of the Harding family were prominent in the firm and took shares when the Ltd company was formed in 1894. William Henry was the ironworks agent and Joshua the ironworks manager at Ford Green. Later, Charles Bruce Harding was the managing director of Robert Heath & Sons Ltd and, later still, Robert Heath & Low Moor Ltd. STAFFORDSHIRE COUNTY RECORD OFFICE: D5420/8

as we shall see, Heaths built their own line to connect with existing operations at Brown Lees and Black Bull.

Eventually, agreement was reached on the basis of a fourteen year lease with options to extend, at a minimum rent of £400 per annum (that is if at any time the mines were not being worked) and a Royalty of 1s per ton of calcined ironstone and for the coal but only if it could be worked at a profit, £33 6s 8d per foot thick per acre. Any coal and slack used for calcining the ironstone or in the boilers for the pit engines to be Royalty free. Chatterley-Whitfield was at liberty to work the lower seams of coal if and when it wanted to and at the same Royalty fee. In consideration of Hazlehurst agreeing to Heaths removing the barrier, he wanted 50% of the Royalties on the coal in the barrier, although this was part of the existing Chatterley-Whitfield estate. This aspect was eventually agreed at 40%. Heaths, incidentally, expected to get 1,000 tons of calcined ironstone a week, after about twelve months of development work. The sub-lease was eventually signed on 29th August 1907.[121]

There is no evidence that Heaths used the Turnhurst shafts for either ironstone or coal mining but they were used for ventilation and pumping in connection with the adjacent Newchapel Colliery. Newchapel was a very old pit, dating from before 1857; on 25th March of that year, its owner, E. Brayford, leased the surface and mineral rights for twenty-one years to W. Sutton. On 12th November 1860, this lease was assigned to Robert Heath and a further one was entered into by

A note on Robert Heath & Sons Ltd headed paper regarding the output and water levels at Newchapel Colliery, dated 5th October 1895. The minerals in this case were held on lease from the Grosvenor Estate and the note is addressed to John H. Cole, Heaths' mining engineer. STAFFORDSHIRE COUNTY RECORD OFFICE D5420/8

Heaths for another twenty-one years from 25th March 1878.[122] This pit was often referred to locally as Brayford's and had primarily been sunk for the Burnwood ironstone. In 1896, there were 140 men employed underground and 21 above; William Cole was the manager.[123] Most of the coal raised at this pit was used on the colliery bank at a mine-hearth to calcine the ironstone, before it was moved by rail for use in the blast furnaces at Black Bull. Evidence exists suggesting that Heaths' also reopened part, at least, of the Lane Ends Colliery, likewise for the extraction of ironstone. In 1891 for example, 1,039 tons are quoted has having been mined during the midsummer period.[124] On 25th March 1896, Heaths had entered into an earlier sub-lease from Chatterley-Whitfield Collieries, in this case mineral rights on the Wedgwood mineral estate, which it is assumed might have been got via either the Newchapel or Lane Ends shafts. However, there is also the possibility that in this case some or all of the ironstone was brought to the surface at Brown Lees Colliery, which was a Heath owned pit. As a matter of interest, this particular lease was part of an agreement between Heaths and Chatterley-Whitfield to maintain a barrier between the coal and ironstone worked by each company. As the underground workings approached each other at and around Chell Heath, there was a risk of joining, with dangers to both ventilation and drainage. The barrier of coal referred to above was not broached until after the 1947 Nationalisation of the coal mining industry.

It was the expansion of operations at Newchapel that led to the underground workings being connected with those at Turnhurst. New ventilating and pumping equipment was installed and, to provide transport for coal and other materials, Heaths extended the private railway that served Newchapel Colliery, along the ridge of high ground to Turnhurst. The railway to Newchapel left Heaths' mineral line between Black Bull and Birchenwood, west of the pit at Brown Lees, climbing onto the ridge. It is perhaps worth mentioning at this juncture, that the line to Newchapel actually pre-dated the one to Birchenwood. There were two later leases entered into by Heaths, for mineral rights of the Burnwood ironstone that could be accessed from the shafts at Newchapel. The first was dated 23rd September 1912 from the Sutcliffe Estate and the second, on 23rd April 1917, from D.W.W. Grosvenor & Others. In both cases, they extended the underground workings in a northerly direction. For a number of years around the turn of the century, W.S. Coe was Heaths' manager at Newchapel, also serving the same role at another Heath pit, the Brownhills Colliery at Tunstall.

At Newchapel, there was a landsale wharf, often referred to locally

as Packmoor, as the two villages are pretty much contiguous. The private mineral railways were worked by a fleet of 4- and 6-wheeled saddle tank locomotives, most of which had been built by Robert Heath & Sons and its successor, Robert Heath & Low Moor Ltd,[125] in the extensive workshops at Black Bull. The Heath locomotive fleet was, at various times, spread around its numerous sites, including the Ford Green collieries and iron works at Norton, the Ravensdale Forge near Chatterley and Parkhouse Colliery between Newcastle-under-Lyme and Talke.[126] During the First World War, it is possible that small quantities of ironstone were raised at Turnhurst but both Newchapel and Turnhurst closed towards the end of the war, probably as late as 1918. In 1917, there were still 123 men employed underground at Newchapel, with a further 42 above. The mineral line as far as Newchapel continued in use after closure of the colliery, to serve the landsale wharf mentioned above, which was adjacent to the road from Newchapel to Great Chell. The actual date this line and the wharf closed appears to have gone unrecorded but it was probably some time in 1964, certainly no later. Both the line and the wharf are known to have still been in use towards the end of 1962.

ABOVE: Edward Brownfield Wain (1861-1925) was the son of Joseph Renshaw Wain, the liquidator of the Chatterley Iron Company. Trained like his father as a mining engineer, E.B. Wain became under-manager at Whitfield Colliery as early as 1882 and general manager in 1886. He was later and until his death, the managing director of Chatterley-Whitfield Collieries Ltd.

RIGHT: A portion of the 1878 first edition of the 25 inch OS map for Turnhurst. The railway line to the left went to the NSR at Goldenhill, whilst the lines on the right were part of the Turnhurst Branch Railway, which ran to the Biddulph Valley line.

The junction at Brown Lees of the two Robert Heath lines, as seen on 16th August 1953. The line branching off to the right ran to the Birchenwood complex at Kidsgrove, which dated from the period 1897-1898, whilst the set of rails heading straight on were a few years older and served Newchapel. It was the Newchapel line that was extended in 1907 or thereabouts to serve Turnhurst, when Heaths' reopened the shafts there. Newchapel village is on the skyline and the line crosses Stadmorslow Road on the level in the foreground. DR JACK HOLLICK

The site of the Brown Lees Colliery of Robert Heath & Sons, looking west in around 1962. The remaining colliery buildings are to the left, with the headgears just discernible beyond. At this time, the shafts were still in use for ventilation and maintenance purposes. The railway line on the left is the private railway to the Birchenwood coking plant at Kidsgrove. The line to Newchapel and, at an earlier date, onwards to Turnhurst, branched from this line just off the picture, round the corner on the left. JOHN HANCOCK

One of the very pleasing six-coupled saddle tank locomotives built by Robert Heath at Black Bull, is seen here propelling loaded wagons to the landsale wharf at Newchapel on 9th April 1962. The locomotive is No. 16, dating from 1924. The spark arresters were essential in view of the gradients when taking loaded trains of coal from Black Bull to Birchenwood, as well as bringing the empties back. In earlier times, when the ironworks was in operation at Black Bull, prior to 1928, the return trains carried coke for the blast furnaces. ROGER K. HATELEY

A second view of No. 16, taken on the same occasion as the previous photograph. Having deposited the loaded wagons at Newchapel, the locomotive is returning to the colliery 'light engine'. These lovely locomotives of such pleasing proportions were great favourites of mine. Powerful too, with 15ins diameter cylinders and comparatively small, 3ft 7ins diameter driving wheels. It was these 6-wheeled engines – there were three of them – that worked Heaths' own traffic between its various operations on the NSR Biddulph Valley line. The practice continued after the Grouping of the railway in 1923, until the firm went into liquidation in 1929. ROGER K. HATELEY

No. 16 again, this time on 21st March 1958 at Birchenwood, carrying out some shunting before taking a train of empty wagons to Victoria Colliery at Black Bull. It would have arrived earlier with a train of loaded coal wagons for the coking plant. The line between Black Bull (Brown Lees actually) and Birchenwood was built by Heaths in 1897-1898, shortly after the Birchenwood complex and the Clough Hall Estate at Kidsgrove were acquired. It was originally intended to take coke from Birchenwood to Black Bull for use in the blast furnaces. After closure of the colliery at Birchenwood and the furnaces at Black Bull, its role changed, thereafter taking coal from Victoria Colliery to Birchenwood. JIM PEDEN, INDUSTRIAL RAILWAY SOCIETY COLLECTION

This is one of the Robert Heath built 4-wheeled saddle tank locomotives that would have been used on the line from Newchapel to Turnhurst. No. 7 was built at Black Bull in 1916 and is seen here at Victoria Colliery on 14th June 1957. Like the 6-wheeled engines, the 4-wheeled ones also sported large spark arresters and it would have been members of this class that worked the line to Newchapel and Turnhurst when the pits there were being worked by Heaths. All the Heath engines had numbers rather than names and were painted black.

Although the location where this photograph was taken, along with the train, are on the fringe of the subject of this book, it is a particular favourite and gives a real flavour of the industrial lines in the area: the Turnhurst Branch Railway would have looked much the same, albeit with an earlier locomotive. The train is on the former Robert Heath private line that connected Black Bull with Birchenwood. After the iron works closed, the traffic was only in one direction, taking coal for coking at Birchenwood, hence this train en route to Black Bull consists of empty wagons. The engine is one of the Heath-built 6-wheelers, No. 15 of 1915, and the train is just breasting the summit of the steep climb from Birchenwood, with the former colliery dirt tip as a backcloth. Just ahead is the bridge taking the line under the Newchapel to Harriseahead road; Harriseahead village is to the right and Newchapel to the left. The photograph was taken on 8th September 1959. Dr Jack Hollick

LEFT: The view towards Newchapel from Turnhurst, taken in about 1970 and showing the embankment remains of the line Heaths built when the Turnhurst lease was acquired. The Goldenhill to Newchapel road can just be seen top left and the large house alongside the road is Newchapel Vicarage. The church and village are just off the picture to the left. JOHN HANCOCK

ABOVE: This photograph was taken a little further back from the previous one and much earlier, on 26th June 1952. The remains of the formation of the railway can be seen in the foreground and Newchapel church is prominent on the skyline. James Brindley lies in the churchyard there. DR JACK HOLLICK

RIGHT: Taken in January 1971 from almost the same spot as the previous picture, this view is looking in the opposite direction, towards Turnhurst. The embankment of Heaths' line is prominent running across the centre. The large building to the top right is on the approximate site of Turnhurst Colliery. AUTHOR

ABOVE: This view looks towards Black Bull, almost at the junction of the lines to Newchapel and Birchenwood. Victoria Colliery and its dirt tip are in the background. The remains of the low embankment of the line to Newchapel are on the right, with the route of the line to Birchenwood on the left; the track had been lifted during the period 1965 to 1966. Just beyond Stadmorslow Road, which runs across the centre of the photograph, is the stub of the lines still in use for wagon storage when this photograph was taken in about 1970. The chimney to the left of the colliery headgears marks the site of Cowlishaw Walker & Company's engineering workshops. Some of the buildings had earlier been the workshops of Robert Heath & Sons, where the locomotives the firm built for its own use were constructed. JOHN HANCOCK

RIGHT: The former cutting almost at the top of Heaths' line at Newchapel, looking towards Black Bull. Taken in about 1970, the Biddulph Valley is in the far distance, while the houses on the right are part of the village of Packmoor. JOHN HANCOCK

A view looking south along the Biddulph Valley Line on 16th August 1953, with the bridge that carried Chatterley-Whitfield Colliery's Whitfield-Pinnox Mineral Railway over it just visible right of centre between the signal and the trees. The photographer was standing on the bridge taking the Chell to Biddulph road under the railway, the present A527. This is the site of the junction of the original line serving Whitfield Colliery, behind the bushes to the left; some of the colliery buildings can be seen on the skyline to the right of the small trees. The junction for the line to Turnhurst was on the right, just beyond the bridge parapet by the lineside bush. The signal is the Whitfield Sidings Up distant. DR JACK HOLLICK

Chatterley-Whitfield Colliery, a view looking due west in 1905. The pit shafts are, from right to left, Platt, Institute and Middle. On the skyline, partly obscured by the steam between the two left hand headgears, can just be discerned the remains of Turnhurst Colliery.

VIII
THE FINAL YEARS AND A FEW ODD ITEMS

On 12th March 1904, Hazlehurst wrote to the NSR from Cold Ashby Hall, to terminate the agreement for the junction of the Turnhurst Branch from 30th of June. The siding agreement called for three months notice on either side but as the NSR minutes are silent on the matter we are no wiser as to what arrangements might have been agreed.[127] What is certain, however, is that by the time Hazlehurst made his request, traffic had ceased to use the branch as all the collieries concerned had closed. As events turned out apart from the limited use of Turnhurst by Heaths as outlined above, they did not reopen. What is particularly interesting is that, despite all the vicissitudes regarding ownership and leasing of the mines at Turnhurst, Chell and Oxford, the Turnhurst Branch Railway seems to have remained in Hazlehurst's personal ownership until it ceased to be used.

We do not know a great deal about how the line and sidings were operated, always shown in those NSR *Working Time Tables* (WTT) we have access to, as Chell Siding. In the 1879 and 1896 WTTs, on average there were two ordinary goods trains shown as calling there in each direction, spending about 10-15 minutes to shunt. This would also encompass any time taken to shunt Chatterley-Whitfield Colliery traffic but, as mentioned earlier, this would be quite small once the colliery company opened its own line to Tunstall. A rather complicated set of engine whistles are outlined in the January 1893 *Appendix to the WTT* for various shunting moves at the Chell Siding. The possibility exists that, under special arrangements, the NSR may on occasions have worked traffic along the branch with its own engines. This might for example, have taken place if the colliery engine(s) were under repair and, as there never seems to have been many of them, this possibility cannot be discounted.

As late as 24th November 1915, Hazlehurst made a lease agreement with Chatterley-Whitfield Collieries Ltd for additional mines on the Chell Estate. By this time he was quite an old man; remember we first heard of him back in 1863, when he would have been 33 years old. He died on 26th January 1918 at the age of 87, give or take a year. His estate was valued at £100,766 15s 11d, an enormous sum of money in those times, equivalent in today's values to about £2,125,000. However, this was a gross figure and the net sum was much less, at £18,123. Presumably, along with his assets, were significant liabilities. While he left a number of relativity small legacies to various folk, including some of his staff and servants as well as his wife Blanche, the bulk of the estate was placed in trust with his executors. Among their number was Archibald Douglas, maybe the same civil engineer mentioned several times earlier, although on this occasion described as a solicitor of Newcastle-under-Lyme. In any event, this might confirm that some at least of Hazlehurst's more pressing liabilities were in connection with his Chell and Turnhurst mining estates. The will specifically mentions mining interests, although not their location. Such income as the estates generated, after paying all expenses and liabilities, was for the benefit of his wife. On her death, the estate passed to Joseph Hall Salkeld of Runcorn, another of his executors and trustees and

the recipient of one of the small legacies mentioned above – in this case £100.

James Wright Beswick and his sons John and Gilbert, in 1894 formed what became the well known pottery and china manufactory trading under the style of J.W. Beswick, latterly at the Globe Street Works in Longton. In 1936, the firm became John Beswick Ltd, famous for its range of china figures including the well-known Beatrix Potter *Peter Rabbit* characters. In 1969, Beswicks sold out to Royal Doulton, who continued to market the figures under the Beswick name until 1989, after which they were absorbed under the Doulton brand.[128]

Two more issues need concern us before bringing this story to

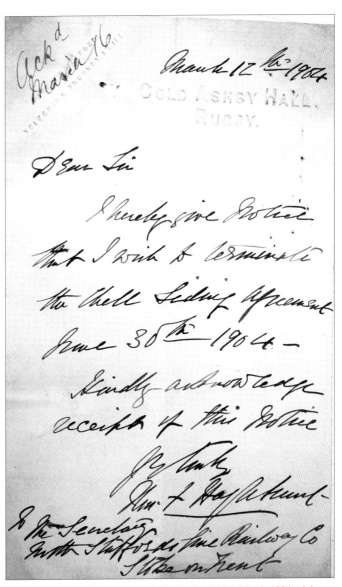

Letter from T.F. Hazlehurst to the NSR, dated 12th March 1904, giving notice to terminate his siding agreement for the Turnhurst Branch. NATIONAL ARCHIVES: RAIL 532/175

a close. In 1952, the late Dr J.R. (Jack) Hollick wrote a private paper which he circulated among his friends, entitled *The Turnhurst Line*. He describes how Tunstall was (and to a small extent still is) the market town for Biddulph but with no direct rail connection between the two. He goes on to mention a proposal, in the period 1880 to 1890, for a direct railway connection between Biddulph and Tunstall, in effect connecting the Biddulph Valley and Potteries Loop lines. The Turnhurst Branch would have been used, extended from Turnhurst down the other (west) side of the high ground, to join the Loop Line just north of Pitts Hill station. The author goes on to mention that survey pegs were installed between Turnhurst and Pitts Hill, and many of them remained in place until some time after 1930. It would appear that this information came from George Conway, at the time the paper was written the station master at Norbury, on the Ashbourne Branch. In earlier times he had been stationed at Ford Green. There is no mention of this scheme in the NSR minute books, while numerous other schemes that never came to fruition are outlined in some depth. I have found no trace of it in any other documents either, despite an extensive search. If the line had been built it would have been an extremely difficult one to work and, in any event, the NSR never seemed to show a great deal of enthusiasm for passenger traffic on the Biddulph Valley line north of Milton Junction. At the best there were three or four trains each way, with no Sunday service. Not only was the service sparse to say

the least but none of the trains were timed to be of use to the locals employed at the mines and ironworks served by the line. In fact, for a number of years, Chatterley-Whitfield Colliery provided a passenger train service for its employees between Bucknall, where it also owned pits, Whitfield and Biddulph. These trains consisted of old coaches loaned or hired from the NSR and the colliery locomotives, some of which had the vacuum brake fitted to comply with Board of Trade regulations.[129] The LM&SR never improved matters and closed the line to regular passenger traffic as early as July 1927, indeed, the first of the ex-NSR lines to lose its passenger service. Excursion trains, however, continued to use the line at holiday times well into British Railways days, with the last ones in the early 1960s. The line closed completely beyond Norton Colliery at Ford Green in January 1976, after Chatterley-Whitfield Colliery ceased coal winding. It was cut back further, to Milton Junction, in June the following year after Norton Colliery closed.

The second issue, also from the private paper mentioned above, concerns one of the colliery locomotives. The author claims that on one occasion when the '*Chell Colliery owed the NSR money*', a locomotive belonging to the colliery was impounded after being '*encouraged to pull well over Turnhurst Junction*' and was removed to Stoke until the money was paid! As with the proposed line to Tunstall, the NSR minutes are silent on this matter, while frequently going into some detail when bills were unpaid by colliery companies, as well as others having private sidings. I have to say, therefore, as with the projected line, I find this story hard to accept, although I am sure knowing Jack as well as I did, he would only have been relaying in good faith what he had been told, having first established the bona fides of his informants.

The Biddulph Valley line of the NSR closed in sections: Congleton Lower Junction to Congleton Upper Junction on 1st December 1963; Heath Junction to Brunswick Wharf at Congleton on 15th January 1969. The line from Ford Green to Heath Junction was converted to single track on 19th February 1967. Chell, Chatterley-Whitfield Colliery Sidings to Heath Junction closed in January 1976; Ford Green to Chell in January 1977; Milton Junction to Ford Green in June 1977. The section between Stoke and Milton Junction and the branch to Leek Brook, was taken out of use on 21st February 1989 but remains in situ and is the subject of a possible reopening by the Staffordshire & Moorlands Railway Company. At Leek Brook Junction it connects with the preserved Churnet Valley Railway, running south to Cheddleton and the Churnet Valley. Connection is also made at Leek Brook with the line to Caldon Low, the latter already reopened for occasional excursion traffic by the Staffordshire & Moorlands Railway Company, in conjunction with the Churnet Valley Railway. Passenger traffic on the Biddulph Valley line beyond Milton Junction ceased on 1st January 1927 and between Stoke and Leek on 7th May 1956.

Robert Heath & Sons' Brown Lees Colliery, a photograph dating from the late 1930s. Coal winding would have ceased at this time, although the shafts were retained for drainage and ventilation. The main line siding connection, which was taken out in September 1939, had latterly been used for the removal of ironworks slag. However, the site was also served by Victoria Colliery's internal railway system.

ACKNOWLEDGEMENTS

In unravelling the story presented here, I have freely delved into the records and papers at the National Archives, the Staffordshire County Record Office, the House of Lords Records Office, the British Library Newspaper Library at Colindale, the London Metropolitan Archives at the Guild Hall Library in London, along with the Keele University Archives. I am extremely grateful to the staff at all seven depositories for help and assistance given. At the National Archives, I have made an extensive study of the records of the NSR, in particular the minute books of both the Directors and Traffic & Finance Committee meetings, along with other relevant documents. The NSR records are held under reference RAIL 532. I have also studied the papers relating to the various companies registered under the Companies Acts, which are held under references BT31, BT41 and J, in connection with the companies mentioned here. The House of Lords Record Office contains an enormous amount of information on railways projected and built, along with verbatim copies of all the various debates and select committee minutes. At the Staffordshire County Record Office are the deposited plans of railways and canals projected and built, along with a wealth of other information. At that depositary I have, in particular, waded deeply into the files under references D3272/1/10/5/1-53, which consist of papers relating to the Turnhurst, Chell and Oxford mineral estates. I have not listed all the specific references in the footnotes but I would recommend any reader wanting further details to consult these papers. In the archives at Keele University are a number of minute books and other documents relating to Chatterley-Whitfield Collieries and its predecessor, the Chatterley Iron Company Ltd. They largely consist of minute books, both for the directors and the colliery officials, part of the William Jack Collection deposited by his family. Bill was employed by the colliery company and later the NCB, when he managed to rescue these priceless volumes which were, quite literally, being thrown away. What I have attempted to do, within the constraints of a reasonable amount of space, is extract and interpret sufficient information to give a succinct and coherent narrative of the various events that took place. It is, of course, left to my readers to judge how successful or otherwise I have been. Where secondary source material has been consulted, I have attempted to cross reference any facts with such primary source material as I have been able to locate.

On a more personal front, help on historical matters has come from the late Bill Jack, a fountain of information on mining and heavy industry in North Staffordshire. Bill had allowed me access to the Chatterley-Whitfield Colliery minute books that were in his care at the time and, as mentioned above, now part of the William Jack Collection, deposited in Keele University Library. As a result of this bequest by his family, I have been able to make a much more extensive study of these volumes. John Hancock and Derek Wheelhouse of Biddulph, both experts in their local area, have cast their eyes over what I have written and made many helpful suggestions. John is deserved of particularly special thanks, not only for his generosity in loaning me and allowing use of his photographs, but also in recently trudging the ground on my behalf to note and photograph such that remains today of all that activity of so long ago. This has enabled me to expand enormously in describing the existing remains in Appendix II, by way of a tour round the area. Bill Dickins has helped with the Hartley, Arnoux & Fanning records, Bob Darvill and Roy Etherington regarding the old Aveling & Porter engine discovered at Brown Lees in 1993, and Vic Bradley with the location of Oak and Bromfield collieries. The late Bernard Holland, extremely knowledgeable on private owner wagons used in North Staffordshire, kindly made his researches available, enabling me to compile the comprehensive list that appeared in *Industrial Locomotives of North Staffordshire*, details of which can be found in the footnotes. Frank Jux helped in pointing out to me some documents in the National Archives I had otherwise missed. A special word of thanks to Lloyd Boardman, latterly the senior geologist for the Western Area of the National Coal Board, not only for ensuring that the geological issues mentioned here are correct but also for casting his eagle eye over the entire text and making a number of helpful suggestions. Long time friend and collaborator on matters North Staffordshire, Mike Fell, like Lloyd, has passed his eye over the draft and also made many useful suggestions. Mike has also kindly conducted, on my behalf, extensive genealogical studies for several of the characters involved in the story. Roger Hateley has for the umpteenth time come to my assistance with his cartography skills. In deciphering my very rough sketches Roger has made some extremely presentable maps, which I hope will help readers find their way through this rather complicated story. All the photographs and other illustrations are either individually credited, of my taking or from my collection.

In Neil Parkhouse of Lightmoor Press I have found a very capable and sympathetic publisher, who I cannot praise enough in taking on this manuscript of what has to be seen as rather an obscure subject. Bear in mind, dear reader, that almost all of the activity described here was complete by around the turn of the 19th and 20th centuries. I had for some time been contemplating it lying in some dusty depository and never seeing the light of day. As it is, what a splendid job has been made and, in view of the time and effort the research and compilation has taken, the finished book is one of what I feel is my finest literary efforts – perhaps even the best!

I cannot close these remarks without a mention of the late Dr J.R. (Jack) Hollick, for so many years my friend and mentor in almost anything relating to North Staffordshire. I have mentioned Jack many times before in my literary efforts but I make no apology for doing so again on this occasion. Jack befriended me from an early age, made all his long years of research available when I had absolutely nothing to offer in return, except that is, my unbounded enthusiasm and thirst for information. I just wanted to learn all I could about my beloved North Staffordshire and Jack never let me down! Last but by no means least, my dear wife Angela, who puts up so lovingly with all my multifarious idiosyncrasies!

APPENDIX I
MAP REFERENCES FOR THE PRINCIPAL MINING SITES
MENTIONED IN THE TEXT

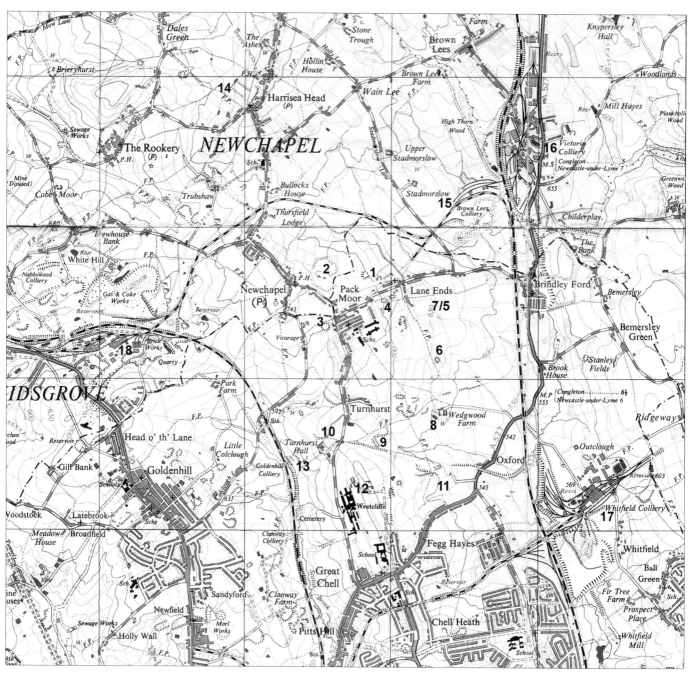

The Ordnance Survey map references, right, all refer to the 1 Inch 7th Series sheet 110, grid square SJ. The numbers relate to those on the map reproduced above, the 1952 Edition 2.5 inch Series sheet. Note that the collieries marked were not all in operation at the same date. The references without a colliery or pit name are very old workings about which little information has been found and, therefore, no name can be attributed to them.

1	869546	
2	865547	Newchapel
3	865544	
4	867545	
5	874545	Lane Ends
6	873542	
7	874544	Lane Ends
8	872538	Wedgwood
9	869535	
10	866536	Turnhurst
11	874533	Oxford
12	868533	Chell
13	863537	Rising Lark

The references below are for other collieries mentioned in the text and numbered above.

14	860559	Harriseahead (*closed*)
15	877551	Brown Lees (*closed*)
16	879555	Victoria
17	884532	Chatterley-Whitfield
18	894543	Birchenwood (*closed*)

APPENDIX II
LIST OF PLANT & MACHINERY, ETC, AT CHELL AND TURNHURST COLLIERIES 1899

This is the list of plant, machinery and other equipment that formed part of the agreement between James Gardiner, as the vendor, and the Turnhurst Coal & Iron Company Ltd, as the purchaser, dated 10th October 1899 and referred to in Chapter VII. Apart from some pronunciation to help the reader, I have left the wording etc, exactly as it appears in the original document. Ref: NA. BT31/8901/65544

1. List of Plant, Machinery etc., at Chell Colliery, Tunstall, Staffs.

One pair horizontal winding engines, slide valves, link motion 25½ inch cylinders, 4ft stroke with round rope drum 10ft diameter now winding out of No's 14 and 16 pits.

One pair horizontal winding engines, slide valves, 24 inch cylinders, 5ft stroke with drum gearing all complete (unfixed) intended for sinking.

One large condensing Tangye pump, steam cylinder 21 inches diameter, water cylinder 7 inch diameter, 3 feet stroke, (now pumping out of No. 14 pit) with steam pipes from boiler and water pipes to top of shaft. Greater part of above is new.

One large pump 21 inch cylinder connected with steam and water pipes now pumping No. 16 pit.

One vertical engine 9 inch cylinder and 14 inch stroke, working saw mill.

One horizontal engine 9 inch cylinder, 4 feet stroke with drum and gearing complete attached to No. 14 pit as an emergency engine.

One De Bay ventilating fan with all gearing complete now ventilating the whole of the workings in 14 and 16 pits.

Two horizontal engines 9 inch cylinders 14 inch stroke working De Bay fan.

One Donkey engine working small slide lathe in fitting shop.

One horizontal condensing engine with drum and all gearing complete now working incline in Twist seam in No. 14 pit.

Three steam boilers No. 1, 28 feet long by 6 feet 6 inches diameter. No. 2, 30 feet long by 6 feet 6 inches diameter. No. 3, 30 feet long by 7 feet diameter. Two flues in each with eight Galloway cross tubes in each flue.

One Donkey pump for feeding boilers.

One double acting Donkey pump, steam cylinder 7 inch diameter 14 inch stroke, water cylinder 4 inch diameter with air vessel etc.

One ventilating fan 3 feet diameter (in shops).

One circular saw on sliding pillars etc.

One small slide lathe in fitting shop.

One locomotive *Clara*, saddle tank, outside cylinders 10½ inch diameter, 20 inch stroke, 6 wheels coupled 3 feet 3 inch diameter, copper firebox and stays, brass tubes etc., comparatively new.

One truck weighing machine (Hinds Patent) to weigh 18 tons.

One weighing machine (Kitchen) to weight 6 tons.

One pit bank weighing machine (Pooley) to weight one ton.

One set single head gears and pulley complete No. 16 pit.

One set double head gears and pulleys complete with upright frame to carry guides at No. 14 pit with necessary ropes and guides.

One set double head gears with pulleys complete, unfixed, intended for sinking.

One Patent coal screen (by Rigg) for loading coal into trucks, also screens constructed from wood for same purpose.
Coal screen at Chell with accommodation for loading six carts at a time.

70 railway waggons, 20 - 8 ton and 50 - 10 ton.

Railway connecting colliery with Biddulph Branch of the North Staffordshire Railway about 900 yards and a railway from Turnhurst Branch to Chell with sidings on the colliery about 1760 yards.

96 yards rails forming cart road from Chell screen to Highway.

All necessary pit wagons, rails and sleepers, jigs, ropes, chains etc., underground.

All iron, timber, oil, machinery and other stores, pit lamps, Blacksmiths, Carpenters and fitters tools etc.

Pipes conveying steam from boilers to dip engines and shops.

Tram road to Chell and all loose material on surface.

The buildings comprise engine houses, machine and lamp houses, Blacksmiths, Carpenters and fitters shops, store room, locomotive shed, brick kilns, offices etc.

Shafts No. 14 sunk to a depth of 270 yards and No. 16 to a depth of 200 yards, cruts, levels, dips etc.

2. List of Plant etc., at the Turnhurst Colliery.

One pair horizontal winding engines, 26 inch diameter cylinders and 4 feet 6 inches stroke with round rope drum (these have been recently erected).

Engine house for ditto, engine beds etc (recently erected).

One large weighing machine (cart and horse).

Two round rope pulleys and sundry loose plant.

About 200 yards of sidings and connections with the loop line Potteries Branch of the North Staffordshire Railway.

Two shafts, 250 yards in depth each 10 feet in diameter sunk to Twist Coal.

APPENDIX III:
THE SCENE TODAY

As I mention in the Acknowledgements, I am very grateful to my friend John Hancock for conducting, in March 2010, an extensive tour of the sites of the collieries and the railways covered in these notes. John lives in Biddulph and in any event knows the area well; indeed, I have used several of his photographs of the surviving remains taken back in 1970. Living, as I do, in far away Kent, this would have been much more difficult for me to achieve. Nonetheless, I do wish I could have accompanied him on his field work. John and I were surprised that so much remains to be seen, despite opencast coal mining and housing development during the last thirty odd years.

Starting with Heaths' line to Newchapel and the site of the colliery there, although the embankment that took the line built by Robert Heath & Sons from Brown Lees to the village has been removed due to opencast coal working, part of its route can clearly be followed, delineated by surviving hedgerows on both sides. This is particularly so on the west side of Stadmorslow Road. It is interesting to speculate that the scene now may be how the land looked when Heaths decided to build their line. There is little to be seen of the former pits that lay just to the north of the Brindley Ford to Packmoor road, east of Newchapel village, or indeed Newchapel Colliery and coal wharf. On the opposite side of the Newchapel to Chell road, nothing remains of Heaths' line to Turnhurst, as this area has been completely covered by housing developments. There is an area of scrub that probably marks the site of one of the former engine pools, for the pit that lay to the west of Heaths' line at Packmoor.

Between Packmoor village and Turnhurst, the remains of the tramway, on the south side of the Packmoor to Chell road and partly in a shallow cutting, can be seen. This served a small pit taking coal to a wharf alongside the road, the site of the former workings being visible too. This was quite a surprise to both John and myself, as neither of us had noticed it on earlier excursions in the area many years ago, when doubtless it should have been even more noticeable. Although situated quite close to them, this pit does not appear to have been connected to the Wedgwood operations.

Moving now to the site of the Lane Ends pit, which was rail connected to the line serving Wedgwood Colliery. There is quite a lot to be seen here, including the site of the pit itself which, judging from the surviving earthworks, may have been a footrail (drift mine)

rather than having any shafts. The railway serving it, all the way to its junction with the line to the Wedgwood pit, can be traced, partly in a shallow cutting. The course is very clear as it crosses a footpath from Lane Ends to Wedgwood, where the steepness of the gradient as it descended to the junction with the Wedgwood line, is very obvious.

Of the Wedgwood line and pit there is also much to be seen. The embankment as the line left the Biddulph Valley line can be clearly located, quite a wide one as it curves away, as doubtless there was a passing loop or sidings located there. Onwards, much of its course can be traced including where the Lane Ends Branch left. At the site of the pit there are two distinct shallow pit mounds, as well as the partly collapsed top of one of the shafts, the void in the surface of the land being very clear and into which John did not venture! The confined nature of these sites might suggest that wagons were propelled, rather than hauled up the gradient, as there would be little room for run-round facilities at the pit sites. This might have been the reason for a run-round facility and sidings at the junction, alluded to above in connection with the wide embankment remains.

Of the Chell and Oxford pits, while the remains of the rubbish mounds can still just about be traced there is nothing of the railways or the coal wharf alongside the Chell to Biddulph road (Biddulph Road, the present A527). This area has been completely obliterated by housing developments, while much of the land where the pits were located has been landscaped as a result of opencast coal working. Of the Turnhurst Colliery site, nothing remains either, as it is completely covered with housing. However, on the opposite side of the Newchapel to Chell road, the course of the railway descending towards the Biddulph Valley line can be traced for some distance, in places a well trodden footpath through a line of quite young trees. The site of the short branch to the pit located to the north can also be seen, along with the obvious site of the pit and dirt tips. This area now appears to be used as an unofficial children's playground. At the site of Newchapel & Goldenhill station, on the NSR Loop Line, which is now a footpath and cycle way, the platform edges can still be located. Also discernible is the former mine loading stage to the south of the station on the Up, Stoke side. Otherwise, this site is surrounded with housing, such that there is no trace of the former line climbing the hill to Turnhurst, or that to the Rising Lark pit.

Harriseahead Colliery in the late 1930s. As mentioned in the caption to the photograph of this colliery which appears on page 4, the surface buildings and headgear of the pits described in this book would have looked very similar to this. Notice, however, the long distance between the headgear and the winding engine house – hence the additional supports for the rope.

ENDNOTES

1. Chell did not become part of the County Borough of the City of Stoke-on-Trent until 1922.
2. Built by the local Wilbraham family of Rode Heath in about 1754, to improve the landscape and serve as a summer house. It was visible from their home.
3. In earlier times spelt New Chapel.
4. All the valleys in this part of North Staffordshire cut into the coalfield and they all carry headstreams of the River Trent.
5. Later and more popularly known as the Trent & Mersey Canal.
6. *The Victoria History of the County of Stafford*, Vol. V111, Oxford University Press 1963.
7. Generalised Vertical Section on 6 inch to 1 mile Geological Survey Map of Staffordshire V11 SW 1951.
8. This fault cuts through the shafts of Sneyd Colliery in Burslem and runs north east of and parallel to the High Lane. This road is the main thoroughfare between Hanley and Chell.
9. A downward fold towards an axis.
10. *The Coal Seams of North Staffordshire: Department of Scientific & Industrial Research*, HMSO 1937.
11. Sometimes spelt Kinnersley, although Kinnersly would on balance seem to be the correct spelling.
12. The Caldon Canal runs from Etruria on the Trent & Mersey, almost 18 miles to Froghall. It opened in 1779.
13. Staffordshire County Record Office (SCRO): Q Rum 27.
14. The Macclesfield Canal runs from Hall Green near Kidsgrove, where it joins the Trent & Mersey, to the Peak Forest Canal at Marple. It opened in 1831 and is just over 26 miles long.
15. It is shown as Trough on the plans and sections but is perhaps, more accurately, Troughstone.
16. John Bailey and the Lancaster brothers owned pits at Gillow Heath, both situated on the projected Gillow Heath Branch.
17. Now known as Dane-in-Shaw, Dane referring to the River Dane which flows through the area.
18. House of Lords Record Office (HLRO): PO/CL/PB6 plan 1839/16.
19. Trading as Bateman & Sherratt of the Salford Iron Works, the firm built a number of early steam engines for pumping purposes at collieries in North Staffordshire. For example, there was one at the Woodshutts Colliery at Kidsgrove, dating from about 1800.
20. In earlier times spelt Knipersley.
21. For a detailed history of coal mining in the Biddulph area up to the end of the 19th century, see the *Transactions of the Biddulph Historical Society*, No. 2 (June 1970) and No. 3 (June 1972), articles by Derek J. Wheelhouse.
22. John Edward Errington (1806-1862), among his many other assignments, was the resident engineer for the Grand Junction Railway under Joseph Locke and later joint engineer with Locke on the Lancaster & Carlisle Railway.
23. HLRO: HL/PO/PB/3, plan 1854 C12; HL/CL/PB/2/22/43. National Archives (NA): BT41/786/4259.
24. The railway company acquired the Macclesfield Canal in 1846.
25. The North Staffordshire Railway Branches Act, 1854 17-18 Vic. Cap cxciv.
26. HLRO: HC/PO/PB/3 plan 1854. NA: BT41/892/5328.
27. *Transactions; Biddulph Historical Society*, No. 3 June 1972; 'Tramways & Railways in the Biddulph Valley 1800-1854', John Hancock. *The Railway Times* 11th June 1864.
28. At the insistence of Parliament insertion of such a clause was quite normal at the time for all railway company Acts, both for completely new lines and extensions to existing ones.
29. NA: Rail532/16; NSR Traffic Committee Minute (TC) No. 2688.
30. NA: MT6/28/41; MT6/28/64; MT6/31/2; MT6/28/49.
31. Often referred to as Heath's, or Heaths, although the signal box nameboard was in the singular.
32. For passenger traffic in July 1864. The remaining sections were opened simultaneously for passenger, goods and mineral traffic.
33. *The Potteries Loop Line,* Allan C. Baker, Trent Valley Publications 1986. ISBN 0948131 20 1.
34. SCRO: D4452/add 1.
35. NA: RAIL 532/17 NSR TC Minute No. 3555.
36. *Industrial Locomotives of North Staffordshire,* edited by Allan C. Baker, Industrial Railway Society 1997. ISBN: 0901096 97 0.
37. NA: RAIL 532/17 NSR TC Minute No. 3554.
38. NA: RAIL 532/16 NSR TC Minute No. 3378.
39. This important highway runs from the outskirts of Hanley to Chell. It was Turnpiked in 1770 and is now part of the B5049.

40. *The Whitfield-Pinnox Mineral Railway;* unpublished paper by the late William Jack & J.R. Hollick. Copy held in the William Jack Collection at Keele University Library.
41. Turnhurst Hall was demolished in 1929. For an excellent history of the Hall and the possibility that James Brindley may have constructed experimental canal locks in its grounds, readers are referred to *James Brindley at Turnhurst Hall* by William D. Klemperer & Paul J. Sillitoe, published by the Stoke-on-Trent City Museum in 1995. ISBN: 1874414 07 6. It contains a number of photographs and maps of the area.
42. *James Brindley: Engineer 1716-1772*, Cyril C.T. Boucher, Goose & Sons 1968.
43. The Hall itself appears not have been part of the estate purchased in March 1760 and may have been purchased independently by James Brindley from the Alsager family. There is mention of parts of the Turnhurst Estate in connection with the probate of the wills of Judith and Mary Alsager, dated 20th June 1792. SCRO D3272/1/10/5/17. For a history of the hall see note 41 above.
44. This is the same Gresley family mentioned in Chapter III, in connection with James Batman acquiring land in the Biddulph area.
45. Sometimes spelt Bellett.
46. *A History of Apedale & Chesterton*, David Dyble, published by the author's widow in 2002. ISBN: 09542199 0 2. *Agents of Revolution; John & Thomas Gilbert – Entrepreneurs,* Peter Lead, University of Keele (undated but 1989 or 1990). ISBN: 09513713 1 2. *The Victoria County History of Staffordshire Vol. V111*, op cit.
47. A Bell Pit is shaped like a bell, hence its name. Coal and ironstone would be worked from a shallow shaft in a circle but only for a short distance as methods of support would be primitive if at all.
48. *The Borough of Stoke-on-Trent,* John Ward, W. Lewis & Sons, London, 1843.
48A. Robert-Innes (formerly Robert Percival Innes), a native of Norwich, joined the Bengal Army in 1843 and saw action in the 1st Sikh War (1845-1846) at the battles of Sobraon and Ferozeshah with the 1st Bengal European Fusiliers. He retired with the honorary rank of Lieutenant-Colonel.
49. The Oak Pits Colliery Company Ltd was originally registered on 10th March 1866 as the Welsh Coal & Mineral Oil Company Ltd, to undertake mining and associated operations at Mold. On 7th January 1873, its name was changed; Anderson became a shareholder somewhere between 1867 and 1872. The Company was in liquidation in July 1882. The only other connection with North Staffordshire would appear to be through Enoch Perrins, also a shareholder, quoted as a surveyor of St. Peter's Chambers, Stoke-on-Trent. NA: BT31/1236/2907C.
49A. Anderson was a native of Liverpool and by the age of 16 a solicitors articled clerk. In the 1861 Census, he is described as a solicitor in practice and a member of the 1st Lancashire Rifle Volunteer Corps.
50. Calcining is a process of burning iron ore to remove moisture and carbon dioxide, to oxidize the ore into ferric-oxide ready for the blast furnace. In reducing the burden, if it is undertaken at the site where the ore is mined, it reduces transports costs and logistics in moving the ore to the furnaces.
51. *Birmingham Post* 18th December 1872.
51A. *Birmingham Daily Post*, 6th June 1874.
51B. NA. C30/3077.
51C. While the Butty System had been quite common in many coalfields in the early part of the 19th century, it was far less so by this time.
51D. Unfortunately, the significance of this name is not apparent; no more does it help identify the parentage of the locomotive.
52. NA: BT31/1794/6832.
53. From 1878, the Birmingham Railway Carriage & Wagon Company Ltd of Smethwick.
54. *The London Gazette* on 4th December 1886, in a report on Attenborough's bankruptcy, listed a whole range of other organisations he was involved with. They included Stenson & Company of Brixworth and Spratton; Lower Resolven Colliery Company; Strata Florida Lead Mine Company; Roe & Company, silversmiths and jewellers in London. His address was given as Great Queen Street in London, as well as Whitley Grove in Reading where he was farming land. It would appear that from his assets, 9d was payable for every £1 that had been invested.
55. Information from Bill Dickins; Hartley, Arnoux & Fanning Company records held privately.
56. NA: RAIL 532/16 TC Minute No's 3143; 3378; 3406; 3418; 3440.
57. The revision date of this map was 1898.
58. NA: RAIL 970/1: In October 1882, the Wedgwood Colliery Company was complaining to the NSR that its empty wagons were being seriously delayed in transit between Longton and Chell. The colliery may have been sending coal to Longton gas works at this time.

59. For a detailed resume of the current remains of most of the pits and railways mentioned in this book, refer to Appendix II

60. Became Newchapel & Goldenhill from 1st January 1913.

61. Many years later, probably early in the last century, the Birchenwood Colliery Company acquired the Rising Lark shaft, where a pump was installed to draw water from the abandoned workings. The water than ran by gravity in a pipe line laid alongside the NSR Loop Line to the coking plants at Kidsgrove. Here it was used to supplement other supplies. Large quantities of water are essential for quenching freshly carbonised coke. This continued until the coking plant closed in 1972.

62. NA: RAIL 532/19 Traffic & Finance Committee (T&FC) Minute No. 9251. In 1867, the separate NSR T&FCs were combined into one body.

63. *Birmingham Post* 16th July 1886.

64. From January 1920, Robert Heath & Low Moor Ltd and, in January 1929, Norton & Biddulph Collieries Ltd.

65. *Industrial Locomotives of North Staffordshire*, op cit.

66. Information from Bob Darvill & Roy Etherington.

67. There were two other Aveling & Porter tramway type locomotives supplied to this customer in 1866 but they were smaller machines and can therefore be discounted.

68. David Cole in his book does, however, mention a partnership of Brassey & Wythes and Lucas Brothers, engaged in construction of the East London Railway line from Wapping to New Cross in 1865. This might indicate that this is where the three Aveling engines were initially employed. Cole also mentions that one of the engines was used by Brassey, Ogilvy & Harrison on a contract for the L&NWR – the Wolverhampton to Walsall line in 1867.

69. *Industrial Locomotives of North Staffordshire*, op cit.

70. SCRO: D3272/1/10/5/24.

71. *People of the Potteries*. Edited by Denis Stuart, University of Keele 1985. ISBN: 0903160 23 4.

72. In June 1872, Homer had purchased the leaseholds of Whitfield and Oxford collieries, subsequently conveying them to the Chatterley Iron Company Ltd. In 1872, the Chatterley Company acquired the Whitfield Colliery Company and, on 17th January 1891, the name of the company was changed to Chatterley-Whitfield Collieries Ltd. Chatterley ironworks closed in 1891 (with a brief re-opening 1899-1901) and the colliery was vested in the National Coal Board on nationalisation of the coal industry on 1st January 1947.

73. SCRO: D3272/1/10/5/29.

74. The sub-lease was agreed for a period of seven years from 3rd May 1900, back to back with the head lease from Homer's executors.

75. Keele University Archives. William Jack Collection, Chatterley-Whitfield Colliery Officials Minute Books No's 3 and 4.

76. NA: BT31/8901/65544. *The King*, issue of 7th April 1900, prospectus of proposed company.

77. *People of the Potteries*, op cit. Census of England 1841.

78. At various times he also traded as a pawn broker and farmed 25 acres of land.

79. *Staffordshire Potters*, R.K. Henrywood, Antique Collectors Club 2002. ISBN: 185149 37 0.

80. NA: RAIL 532/17 NSR TC minute No 4603.

81. SCRO: D3272/1/10/5/52. *North Wales Chronicle*, 15th August 1857.

82. Sometimes spelt Sandiway, which is the name of the adjacent village.

83. *Kelly's Handbook to the Titled, Landed & Official Classe*, 1895, Kelly & Co.

84. Information from the late William Jack.

85. SCRO: D3272/1/10/5/18.

86. *Staffordshire Potters*, op cit.

87. SCRO: D3272/1/10/5/18.

88. Unfortunately, a company file compiled by the Joint Stock Companies Registrar does not appear to have survived in the National Archives. Neither is the company listed in the list of companies on the Register from 1856 to 1920. I am, therefore, sceptical that registration for Limited liability ever took place.

89. *Birmingham Daily Post*, 25th April 1863.

90. This coal seam is often referred to by several other names; Gin Mine, Pottery or Doctors Mine, perhaps the former being the more common, at least in other parts of the coalfield.

91. NA: RAIL 532/17 NSR TC Minute No's 3964; 4608. RAIL 532/13 NSR Finance Committee minute No. 9487 of 5th September 1865, records £233 9s 9d being paid to James Lockett for works undertaken on new sidings at Chell for Mr Hazlehurst.

92. NA: RAIL 970/1: The NSR Weekly Notice for the period 12th to 19th August 1882, refers to a new signal box and signalling arrangements at Chell Sidings, brought into use on 13th August. For the period 30th September to 7th October 1882, there is reference to a *'signal being placed on the Turnhurst Colliery Branch for the purpose of stopping the colliery engine working on this line'*. Presumably,

hitherto it had been the practice of the colliery engine driver to exceed his authority!

93. SCRO: D3272/1/10/5/52.

94. SCRO: D3272/1/10/5/59.

95. In 1873, Robert Beswick junior was elected to membership of the North Staffordshire Institution of Mining & Mechanical Engineers. The following year, his manager at Chell, William Scragg, was also elected.

96. NA: BT31/2040/8876.

97. Luke Bishop was elected to membership of the North Staffordshire Institution of Mining & Mechanical Engineers in 1875. He was then described as a colliery proprietor at Chell Colliery.

98. NA: BT31/12077/9235.

99. NA: RAIL 532/19 NSR T&FC No. 9672.

100. This was the same gentleman who had acted in a similar capacity for the Wedgwood Coal & Iron Company Ltd – as noted earlier.

101. NA: BT31/2077/9235. SCRO: D3272/1/10/5/52.

102. *Reports of Inspectors of Mines 1883*. HMSO.

103. Note that James is quoted as the middle Christian name rather than Francis; this is, however, considered to be a transcription error.

104. NA: BT31/3836/24130.

105. NA: RAIL 532/174.

106. NA: RAIL 970/1.

107. Reports of HM Inspectors of Mines 1889. HMSO 1890. *Birmingham Daily Post*, 15th November 1889.

108. NA: BT31/8901/65544.

109. *Industrial Locomotives of North Staffordshire*, op cit.

110. Later absorbed by the Taff Vale Railway and subsequently part of the Great Western Railway.

111. *The Cheadle Railway*, Allan C. Baker, Oakwood Press 1979. *The Cheadle Collieries and their Railways*, Allan C. Baker, Trent Valley Publications 1986. ISBN: 0948131 12 8.

112. SCRO: D3272/1/10/5/57.

113. London Metropolitan Archives: Guild Hall Library, Stock Exchange Annual Company Reports

114. The wagon lease was with the British Wagon Company Ltd of Rotherham. This firm had a workshop at Kidsgrove where it undertook wagon maintenance and repairs. The liquidator had asked Hazlehurst if he could help in taking over the lease for these wagons (a figure of £664 was outstanding according to the wagon company) of which there were 70. Hazlehurst passed this request on to Chatterley-Whitfield, where it was declined.

115. NA: J13/3837.

116. This was a generally accepted type of arrangement on Royalty payments; in some cases it also allowed for any coal used for calcining ironstone.

117. Keele University Archives. William Jack Collection, Chatterley-Whitfield Colliery Officials Minute Books No's 5 and 6.

118. This was Nasmyth Wilson No. 304 of 1886, *Gidlow*, ex-Ince Coal & Cannel Company of Wigan: it became Chatterley-Whitfield's second locomotive bearing the name *Roger*.

119. This was the first Chatterley-Whitfield locomotive named *Roger*, Manning Wardle No. 388 of 1873.

120. Keele University Archives. William Jack Collection, Chatterley-Whitfield Colliery Officials Minute Books No's 7 and 8.

121. Keele University Archives. William Jack Collection, Chatterley-Whitfield Colliery Officials Minute Books No's 7 and 8.

122. SCRO: D4452/add 1.

123. In 1905, the figures were 231 and 88 respectively.

124. SCRO: D5420/8-9, Newchapel Colliery lease documents.

125. On 6th January 1920, the Heath Company joined forces with the Low Moor Company Ltd of Bradford and became Robert Heath & Low Moor Ltd. In February 1928, a receiver was appointed and the iron and steel works at Norton and Black Bull closed, along with the rolling mills. On 23rd January 1929, a new company was formed to operate the collieries at Black Bull and Norton, Norton & Biddulph Collieries Ltd. The collieries became part of the National Coal Board West Midlands Division, No. 1 North Staffordshire Area on 1st January 1947. Victoria Colliery at Black Bull ceased coal winding on 30th August 1982. Norton had ceased coal winding on 23rd June 1977. Chatterley-Whitfield Colliery ceased coal winding on 16th January 1976.

126. *Industrial Locomotives of North Staffordshire*, op cit.

127. NA: RAIL 532/174.

128. *The History of Beswick*, www.beswick-animals-collectables.co.uk/beswick_history.php. Staffordshire Potteries, op cit, gives the works in 1896 as Baltimore Works, Albion Street, Longton and in 1900, the location as High Street, Longton.

129. *Industrial Locomotives of North Staffordshire*, op cit.